**To John Cleese,
Funny and affectionate friend.
Fellow collector over 45 years.**

Copyright © Chris Beetles Ltd 2024
8 & 10 Ryder Street, St James's
London SW1Y 6QB
020 7839 7551
gallery@chrisbeetles.com
www.chrisbeetles.com

ISBN 978-1-914906-13-8

Cataloguing in publication data is available from the British Library

A Chris Beetles Gallery Publication

With contributions by Chris Beetles, Alexander Beetles,
Phoebe Bowsher, Fiona Nickerson and Phoebe Ross
Edited by Chris Beetles, Alexander Beetles,
Fiona Nickerson and Pascale Oakley-Birch
Design by Pascale Oakley-Birch
Photography by Alper Goldenberg and Giulio Sheaves
Reproduction by www.cast2create.com
Colour separation and printing by Geoff Neal Litho Limited

**Celebrating 40 years
in Ryder Street,
St James's, London**

Front cover:
S R Badmin, *Henley Royal Regatta* [**138**]

Front endpaper:
James John Hill, *Village Days* [**19**]

This page:
Charles Tunnicliffe, *Eagle Owls* [detail of **131**]

Title page:
Henry Nelson O'Neil, *The Girl by the Gate* [**21**]

Pages 136-137:
John Sherrin, *The Gardener's Pride* [**22**]

Back endpaper:
Geraldine Girvan, *White Cloth* [**166**]

Back cover:
Albert Goodwin, *King's Parade, Cambridge* [**60**]

Chris Beetles
Summer Show
2024

CHRIS BEETLES GALLERY

FRANCIS WHEATLEY

Francis Wheatley, RA (1747-1801)

Francis Wheatley is best known as a painter of landscapes, portraits and figures in a sentimental and pretty style. His most popular and notable works were the *Cries of London*, a series of fourteen paintings of London street scenes which were then engraved and published in pairs.

For a biography of Francis Wheatley, please refer to page 138.

1
Going to School
Signed and dated 1795
Watercolour with bodycolour
13 ¾ x 10 inches
Provenance: Luke Gertler Collection

2

Refreshment Time
Signed and dated 1795
Watercolour
13 ¾ x 10 inches
Provenance: Sotheby's, 19 March 1970, lot 47;
Luke Gertler Collection
Exhibited: Leger Galleries, London, 1970, no 27

THOMAS ROWLANDSON

Thomas Rowlandson (1757-1827)

Thomas Rowlandson raised comic art to a new level by representing the panorama of contemporary life with almost unparalleled fluency – adopting lyricism or incisiveness as best fitted the subject. And, in capturing an abundance of picturesque detail, his work provided a parallel to the novels of Henry Fielding or Laurence Sterne.

For a biography of Thomas Rowlandson, please refer to *Chris Beetles Summer Show*, 2017, page 4.

With thanks to Nicholas Knowles for his help in compiling these notes on Thomas Rowlandson.

3
**Gaming at Brook's Club,
or Rooks Waiting for a Pigeon**
Ink and watercolour
5 ½ x 8 ¼ inches

**Gaming at Brook's Club,
or Rooks Waiting for a Pigeon**

Thomas Rowlandson's familiarity with the gaming table is well known and was used often in his work, such as in *A Kick Up at a Hazard Table* (a print of which was produced by John Harris). Grego lists a drawing with the title *Gaming House* as 'a drawing similar to that which serves as a frontispiece to the *Beauties of Tom Brown*' (Grego, vol II, page 431). The print referred to is *Gaming House where a Parcell of sharks meet to bite one another's Heads off!*, a similar composition as the present drawing, with a table of despondent gamblers. The present artwork is one of a number of drawings by Thomas Rowlandson that share the same fundamental composition but with minor differences to the figures and objects that appear. A similar drawing is recorded as being in the collections of the London Museum, entitled *Gaming at Brook's Club* (see John Hayes, *A Catalogue of the Watercolour Drawings* by Thomas Rowlandson in the London Museum, 1960, no 9). Another, entitled *Rooks Waiting for Pigeons* is recorded in Grego as being in the collection of W T B Ashley in 1880 (Grego, vol II, page 417). Another version of this artwork is recorded in the collections of Brown University (Providence, RI), with the title *British Club Scene*.

Bitter Fare, or Sweeps Regaling

'The date of this plate has been altered; it was probably published in 1802, and re-issued later, a common occurrence with Rowlandson's prints. *Bitter Fare, or Sweeps Regaling*, was, as it seems likely, designed as a companion to *Love and Dust* (1792) and it partakes of the same ragged inspiration. In the hovel tenanted by the somewhat undesirable 'Chummey family', smoke is the prevalent element; the sooty company, sufficiently black and begrimed in their own persons, seem perfectly in their element before a smoking fireplace – as they are reposing luxuriously on sacks of soot. The heads of the family are amiably sharing their enjoyments, drinking beer from a pewter measure, and smoking long clay pipes; the sweeper lads, but for a coat of soot comparatively unclad, are revelling amidst the cinders on the hearth, divided between the congenial relaxations of eating porridge and tormenting an unfortunate cat. Brushes, shovels, and the professional belongings of chimney-sweeping are scattered about; the only article of fancy admitted into the establishment is a blackbird, which is possibly present on the ground that its hue offers a resemblance to the general complexion.'

Joseph Grego, *Rowlandson the Caricaturist*, London: Chatto and Windus, 1880, vol II, page 233.

Etchings with alternate dates are in the collections of the Royal Collection Trust (1803) and Metropolitan Museum of Art, New York (1812).

4
Bitter Fare, or Sweeps Regaling
Signed and dated 1802
Ink and watercolour
11 ½ x 8 inches
Literature: Joseph Grego, *Rowlandson the Caricaturist*, London: Chatto and Windus, 1880, vol II, page 233

5
Mercury and the Three Graces
Signed
Ink and watercolour
4 x 5 ½ inches

Mercury and the Three Graces

Thomas Rowlandson held a great interest in classical imagery throughout his career, having first been introduced to the study of ancient sculpture while a student of the Royal Academy Schools. The mythology of the Classical world and the art that it inspired both held a great appeal to him, and was often used as a weapon in his satirical arsenal.

The present drawing is an example of Rowlandson's emulation of Classical beauty. Like many of Rowlandson's Classical images, it is inspired by a print of an old master painting, in this instance the inspiration is possibly Agostino Carracci's etching and engraving of *Mercury and the Three Graces* by Jacopo Tintoretto (1518-1594).

6
The Village Store
Ink and watercolour
4 ¾ x 7 ¾ inches

7

The Coffee House
Ink and watercolour
4 ¼ x 7 inches

Thomas Rowlandson produced many drawings featuring 'eating houses' and 'chop houses', characterised by the high backed wooden booths and large clock. The likelihood that the present drawing is a coffee house is due not only to the lack of food on the tables, but also because the men present are still wearing their hats. In eating and chop houses, the diners' hats were removed.

8

Persecution to the Grave, or enraged Usurers outwitted by death
Watercolour with ink
10 x 14 inches

THOMAS ROWLANDSON

Marshalsea Prison

The notorious Marshalsea Prison, situated in Southwark, London, had housed a variety of prisoners since 1373. By the eighteenth century, it had become known largely as debtors prison, with many prisoners incarcerated for debts of as little as a few pounds. Prisoners were allowed certain freedoms, could conduct business, receive visitors and lovers, and many had their wives and children live with them in the prison. Marshalsea had a kitchen, a public room, and even a tap room, where debtors could drink as much beer as they liked for fivepence a pot in 1815. Prostitutes arrested by the watch were held and bought before the Constable of the night. Thomas Rowlandson produced several other images relating to the rounding up of prostitutes.

Marshalsea Prison was demolished and rebuilt in 1811 after prison reformers had drawn attention to the original site's decaying and ruinous state. Thomas Rowlandson likely produced the present drawing around 1820, by which time the newly rebuilt Marshalsea would have once again become considerably overcrowded. Marshalsea was closed by an Act of Parliament in 1842, with the inmates being moved to Bethlem or the King's Bench Prison.

Marshalsea is known as having featured in a number of Charles Dickens novels, including *The Pickwick Papers*, *David Copperfield* and particularly in *Little Dorritt*, whose main character, Amy Dorritt, was born and raised at Marshalsea. Dickens had first-hand experience of Marshalsea, having seen his father, John, sent there in 1824 for a debt of £40 10 shillings to a baker.

The present drawing is likely to be a preliminary sketch for the drawing that is in the collections of the Boston Public Library (Arthur Heintzelman, *Watercolour Drawings of Thomas Rowlandson from the Boston Public Library*, New York, NY: Watson-Guptill, 1947, page 107).

9
Marshalsea Prison
Ink and watercolour
5 ¾ x 8 ½ inches

WILLIAM PAYNE

William Payne, AOWS (1760-1830)

William Payne was probably the most fashionable drawing master of the day, popular for both his loose, yet clear, application of pigment and his willingness to extend the bounds of the medium of watercolour.

For a biography of William Payne please refer to *Chris Beetles Summer Show*, 2001, page 6.

10
View on the River Dart
Inscribed with title on reverse
Oil on panel
7 ½ x 9 ½ inches

RICHARD WESTALL

Richard Westall, RA (1765-1836)

Richard Westall was born in Reepham, Norfolk in 1765. His father Benjamin Westall was a churchwarden in Norwich, where he was baptised. His mother died when he was young, and following this alongside the bankruptcy of his father, Richard Westall moved to London in 1772 where he would remain for the rest of his life. His father had another son in 1781, William Westall, who also went on to become a notable artist.

In 1779 Richard Westall was apprenticed to a silver engraver and began to produce oil paintings, historical watercolours and book illustrations in London, for which he became renowned. He first exhibited at the Royal Academy in 1784, and was enrolled as student there the following year. He was elected RA ten years later in 1794, and exhibited there regularly until the end of his life. He was especially proficient in the use of gouache and in 1795 was declared by the *St. James's Chronicle* as 'the Founder of a particular School of Drawing in Water-Colours'.

In 1826 he was employed as the drawing master to Princess (later Queen) Victoria. Richard Westall never married and died in 1836, aged 71.

Lady Elizabeth Grey Beseeching Edward IV

Various artistic depictions of Lady Elizabeth Grey Beseeching Edward IV survive, and they refer to her plea to return her late husband's land following his death in 1461 at the Second Battle of St Albans. Usually she is portrayed with her two sons and ladies-in-waiting but in Westall's more intimate scene, he conveys the desperation attached to the pair's first meeting. Lady Elizabeth Grey was a commoner, a widow and a Lancastrian – aspects which would usually forbid her union with King Edward. Nonetheless, three years later Lady Elizabeth Grey and Edward IV married in secret. Controversially, they would go on to rule England together until Edward's death in 1483.

11
Lady Elizabeth Grey Beseeching Edward IV
Signed and dated 1789
Watercolour with bodycolour
12 ½ x 16 ¾ inches

Cardinal Ximenes answering the Grandees, of Spain, who questioned his authority

Francisco Jiménez de Cisneros, referred to in this scene as Cardinal Ximenes, was the Archbishop of Toldeo under Isabella I of Castile. He was known for his religious influence and strict reforms at the turn of the 16th century Spain. When Isabella died in 1504, the natural successor was her daughter Joanna. However, as 'Joanna the Mad' she was deemed unfit to rule Castile, leading to a regency dispute between her father and husband. Ximenes mediated the affair and introduced the Treaty of Villafáfila, allowing Joanna's husband Philip I to hold the King's title and Ferdinand, Joanna's father, to act as co-regent.

A controversial figure at court, Ximenes was regularly challenged by others. Westall depicts Grandees, Spanish noblemen, questioning the Cardinal's position in the dispute before the Treaty was established.

In these two historical paintings by Richard Westall the drama of both compositions, with the arms of the figures outstretched or clutched to their chest, lends the theatrical to two highly atmospheric works. They certainly exemplify the nature of his history painting, with the figures brought like characters to the foreground against a delicately painted set. The heightening in white that can be seen primarily on the clothes of the figures is also a signature of Richard Westall's painting, and a technique for which he became renowned in the late eighteenth century.

12

Cardinal Ximenes answering the Grandees, of Spain, who questioned his authority
Signed and dated 1790
Watercolour with bodycolour
17 x 21 ¼ inches
Exhibited: Royal Academy of Arts, 1790, no 612, as 'Anecdote From The Cardinal Ximenes'

Engraved in Mezzotint by William Ward, published by John Raphael Smith, 14 May 1792

J M W TURNER

Joseph Mallord William Turner (1777-1851)

J M W Turner is undoubtedly one of the most influential and celebrated British artists to have ever lived. Eccentric and controversial, he was highly successful in his own lifetime, achieving considerable wealth, fame and critical acclaim. A prolific painter, watercolourist, etcher and printmaker, upon his death he bequeathed over 19,000 paintings and drawings to the nation. Variously described as a founder of Impressionism and a forerunner of modernist abstraction, J M W Turner elevated landscape painting to pre-eminence through expressionistic studies of light, colour, and atmosphere that were unmatched in their range and sublimity.

Further Reading:
Andrew Wilton, *The Life and Work of J.M.W. Turner*, London: Academy Editions, 1979;
Andrew Wilton, *Turner in his Time*, London: Thames & Hudson, 1987

THOMAS GIRTIN

Thomas Girtin (1775-1802)

Though his career was cut short by his premature death at the age of just twenty-seven, Thomas Girtin was still able to achieve much in his lifetime, to the extent that he is today considered one of the most influential of painters in watercolour. Girtin played a significant role in establishing watercolour as its own aesthetic medium, it having formerly been used largely to colour engravings. Along with his contemporary J M W Turner, he was employed as a boy to wash in skies for architectural drawings and in colouring prints for a printseller. In his final years, he evolved a bold, Romantic style, demonstrating a mastery of the genre that, had he lived longer, would have rivalled the reputation of Turner.

Further Reading:
Thomas Girtin and David Loshak, *The Art of Thomas Girtin*, London: A & C Black, 1954

Folkestone Harbour

This drawing of Folkestone Harbour is the product of a remarkable collaboration between Thomas Girtin (1775-1802) and Joseph Mallord William Turner (1775-1851), embarked upon when both artists were still teenagers. Girtin and Turner were employed by Dr Thomas Monro (1759-1833), art patron and Principal Physician of Bethlem since 1792, to copy the rough and unfinished drawings of the artists John Robert Cozens (1752-1797), Edward Dayes (1763-1804) and John Henderson (1764-1843), depicting coastal scenery and shipping on the south coast of England. The joint ownership of these drawings is suggested by the artist Joseph Farington (1747-1821), who recorded details of the undertaking in his diaries. He records that Henderson lent his 'outlines for this purpose' (Farington, *Diary*, 30 December 1794) and that 'Girtin drew in outlines and Turner washed in the effects', with Turner receiving '3s.6d each night' though 'Girtin did not say what He had' (Farington, *Diary*, 12 November 1798).

The present artwork is the only view of Folkestone that has so far been identified from the 'Twenty-Six sketches at Dover and Folkestone, in blue and Indian ink' that were sold at Dr Monro's posthumous sale, possibly at Christie's, in 1833. Though majority of the drawings sold in this 1833 sale were attributed to Turner alone, a pioneering article in 1984 by the Turner scholar, Andrew Wilton, established the joint ownership of many of the drawings (Wilton, pages 8-23).

Further Reading:
Kenneth Garlick, Angus Macintyre, Kathryn Cave and Evelyn Newby, [eds], *The Diary of Joseph Farington*, 17 vols,New Haven, CT and London: Paul Mellon Centre for Studies in British Art, 1978–98;
Greg Smith, thomasgirtin.com, part of the Paul Mellon Centre for Studies in British Art;
Andrew Wilton, 'The "Monro School" Question: Some Answers', *Turner Studies*, vol 4, no 2, Winter 1984, pages 8-23

J M W Turner (1775-1851) and Thomas Girtin (1775-1802)

13
Folkestone Harbour
Watercolour and pencil
6 ¼ x 10 inches
Provenance: Dr Thomas Monro (1759-1833);
His posthumous sale, possibly Christie's, 28 June 1833, lot 81
as 'Twenty-six sketches at Dover and Folkestone, in blue and Indian ink' by 'Turner';
Sotheby's, 11 November 1976, lot 64 as by Joseph Mallord William Turner

JOHN CONSTABLE

John Constable, RA (1776-1837)

One of the most significant and important British artists of the 19th century, John Constable is best known for his paintings of the English countryside, particularly those representing his native Stour Valley, Suffolk an area that came to be known as 'Constable Country'. His highly original approach to landscape painting and his lifelong dedication to the genre resulted in a remarkable body of work that has ensured his contribution to the development of British landscape art is rivalled only by that of his contemporary, J M W Turner.

For a biography of John Constable, please refer to page 139

A Barn at the Edge of a Wood, East Bergholt

The present drawing, previously thought to be lost, is highly likely to be the same drawing that was exhibited as *A Barn and Trees* in the exhibition, 'Drawings by John Constable R.A.' at the Dunthorne Gallery in Vigo Street, London, in June 1936. It was subsequently sold as part of the collection of a Dr H A C Gregory at Sotheby's on 20 July 1949. The drawing was referenced in Graham Reynolds' *The Early Paintings and Drawings of John Constable* (1996) as 'present whereabouts unknown'.

John Constable spent much of the summer of 1802 in East Bergholt, the place of his birth, accompanied by his friend and patron, Dr John Fisher, where it is likely this drawing was produced. The summer of 1802 marked a considerable moment in Constable's career, when he refused the stability of a post as drawing master at a military academy in order to dedicate himself to landscape painting and the study of nature. In a letter to Robert Dunthorne dated 29 May 1802, Constable wrote:

'For these few weeks past, I believe I have thought more seriously of my profession than at any other time of my life; of that which is the surest way to excellence. I am just returned from a visit to Sir George Beaumont's pictures with a deep conviction of the truth of Sir Joshua Reynold's observation, that "there is no easy way of becoming a good painter." For the last two years I have been running after pictures, and seeking the truth at second hand. I have not endeavoured to represent nature with the same elevation of mind with which I set out, but have rather tried to make my performances look like the work of other men. I am come to a determination to make no idle visits this summer, nor to give up my time to commonplace people. I shall return to Bergholt, where I shall endeavour to get a pure and unaffected manner of representing the scenes that employ me. There is little or nothing in the exhibition worth looking up to. *There is room enough for a natural painter*. The great vice of the present day is *bravura*, an attempt to do something beyond the truth. Fashion always had, and will have, its day; but truth in all things only will last, and can only have just claims on posterity. I have reaped considerable benefit from exhibiting. It shows me where I am, and in fact tells me what nothing else could.'

(C R Leslie RA, *Life and Letters of John Constable RA*, London: Chapman and Hall, 1896, page 17).

14

A Barn at the Edge of a Wood, East Bergholt
Dated 'June 22 1802'
Pencil
6 x 10 ¼ inches
Provenance: Dunthorne Gallery, 1936;
Dr H A C Gregory, 1949
Literature: G Reynolds, *The Early Paintings and Drawings of John Constable*: New Haven, CT: The Yale University Press, 1996

This authenticity of this artwork has been verified by Anne Lyles, former curator of 18th and 19th Century British Art at the Tate and leading expert on the work of John Constable.

SAMUEL PROUT

Samuel Prout, OWS AA (1783-1853)

Despite persistent ill health, Samuel Prout developed as a highly distinctive topographical artist and undertook regular sketching tours, first in Britain and later on the Continent. The resulting images of ancient buildings at their most picturesque were highly popular and influential as exhibition watercolours and, especially, lithographic illustrations.

For a biography of Samuel Prout, please refer to pages 140-141.

15
Wellhead
Signed on reverse
Watercolour
8 ½ x 12 inches

16
Café de la Place, Rouen
Signed
Watercolour
27 ¾ x 20 ½ inches

SAMUEL PROUT

17
Ypres
Watercolour
13 ½ x 9 ¼ inches

SAMUEL GILLESPIE PROUT

Samuel Gillespie Prout (1822-1911)

Samuel Gillespie Prout was born in 1822, the youngest of four children of the artist, Samuel Prout and his wife Elizabeth Gillespie. His intention was to follow his father's profession and his style indicates his father's work was a strong influence on him. He made a tour of France in 1846 and attempted to earn a living as a teacher of drawing but later in his life, as an Evangelical Christian, became increasingly occupied with charitable work. In 1871, he was one of the first to bring relief to starving Parisians after the siege of Paris as an early member of the French Red Cross. He was supposedly employed as a colporteur during the Spanish Carlist Wars (1872-1876) and was a volunteer in the Relief of Khartoum (March 1884-January 1885). At home, he raised and distributed funds for families after the mining disaster at Abercarn colliery in 1878 and wrote a book for the criminals and destitute living in Manchester.

He died in the Devon village of Braunton in 1911.

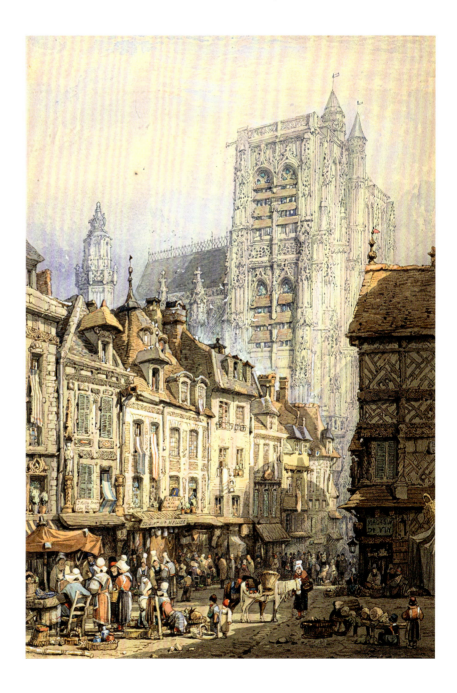

18
Abbeville, Normandy
Watercolour
20 ¾ x 14 inches

The 16th century church of Saint Vulfran is visible in the background.

JAMES JOHN HILL

James John Hill, VPSBA (1811-1882)

Skilled in a range of subjects, including portraits and landscapes, James John Hill became particularly identified with picturesque rural genre scenes, often featuring pretty young peasant women.

For a biography of James John Hill, please refer to
Chris Beetles Summer Show, 2019, page 36.

19

Village Days
Signed
Oil on canvas
11 ¼ x 19 ¼ inches

20

Spring
Signed and dated 1864
Oil on board
11 ½ x 9 ½ inches
Illustrated: *The Illustrated London News*, 9 May 1863, page 504
Exhibited: Society of British Artists Annual Exhibition, Suffolk Street, London, 1863

HENRY NELSON O'NEIL

Henry Nelson O'Neil, ARA (1817-1880)

Born in Saint Petersburg, Russia, O'Neil moved to England with his family at the age of six. In 1836 he entered the Royal Academy Schools and began exhibiting at the RA from 1838. With Richard Dadd and W P Frith, he became a member of the 'Clique', a group of young artists based in St John's Wood who were dissatisfied with the traditionalist methods of the Academy. He was a successful and prolific painter, at ease in most fields, including portraiture, landscape and history but is chiefly remembered for his hugely successful genre scenes, in particular Eastward Ho! of 1857. Emotionally-charged and meticulously detailed, it shows the wives, sweethearts, and families of the troops embarking an army ship at the time of the Indian Mutiny. His equally popular paintings *Home Again* and *Princess Alexandra Landing at Gravesend* were in a similar vein. He exhibited at the Royal Academy until 1879 and at the British Institution for 22 years from 1839. He was elected Associate of the Royal Academy in 1879 and died in London the following year.

21
The Girl by the Gate
Signed with monogram and dated 1861
Oil on board
10 ¼ x 8 ½ inches

JOHN SHERRIN

John Sherrin, RI (1819-1896)

One of the few known pupils of William Henry Hunt, John Sherrin would come to equal his master as a painter of intimate still life compositions and animal subjects.

For a biography of John Sherrin, please refer to *Chris Beetles Summer Show*, 2018, page 50.

22
The Gardener's Pride
Watercolour with bodycolour
13 ½ x 18 ½ inches

23
**Roses on a
Mossy Bank**
Signed
Watercolour
and bodycolour
8 ¼ x 9 ½ inches

24
**Forest Floor Still
Life with Blossom**
Signed
Watercolour with
bodycolour
9 x 11 inches

25

Forest Floor Still Life with Primroses
Watercolour and bodycolour
12 ½ x 18 inches

WILLIAM SIMPSON

William Simpson, RI FRGS (1823-1899)

William Simpson was a pioneering Special Artist; that is a visual journalist sent to record major news stories for illustrated publications. Making his reputation with lithographs of his watercolours of the Crimean War, and even gaining the name 'Crimea Simpson', he later developed a close association with *The Illustrated London News*.

For a biography of William Simpson, please refer to *Chris Beetles Summer Show*, 2015, pages 9-10.

26
Praying Wheels at Soonum
Signed, inscribed with title and 'To S R Hutt' and dated '10th November 1896'
Watercolour
14 ¼ x 10 inches

Praying Wheels at Soonum

William Simpson was commissioned by the London lithography firm, Day and Sons, to travel to India to document sites in and around Delhi associated with the Revolt of 1857 against the rule of the British East India Company. Simpson arrived in Calcutta in 1859 and spent almost three years travelling extensively around the country. He visited Soonum, a small village in the Himalayas, in 1862, shortly before his return to London. During his travels, he produced a large number of rapid pencil drawings which formed the preparatory studies for the watercolours that he completed upon his return to England. The present watercolour, dated 1896, over thirty years after his visit to Soonum, is similar in composition to a work in the collections of the Victoria & Albert Museum dated 1862, suggesting that Simpson worked up multiple watercolours from his preparatory sketches.

Prayer wheels are commonly used in Buddhist and Tibetan culture. Mantras are carved into the wheels and when rotated are said to accumulate positive karma and multiply the efficacy of the mantra carved into them. The wheels recorded at Soonum by William Simpson are positioned so as to be rotated constantly by flowing water. It is said that the water that touches these wheels is blessed and carries purifying powers.

EDWARD KILLINGWORTH JOHNSON

Edward Killingworth Johnson, RWS (1825-1896)

Edward Killingworth Johnson was a Victorian wood engraver, illustrator, watercolourist and painter in oils, specialising in rural genre scenes. He gained much success during the 1860s as a regular contributor to *The Illustrated London News* and latterly *The Graphic*. He exhibited at the Royal Academy and the Society of Painters in Water Colours and throughout his life received much recognition in both his native England and in America with works such as *Tuning Up* and *The Rival Florists*.

For a biography of Edward Killingworth Johnson, please refer to *Chris Beetles Summer Show*, 2018, pages 61-62.

27
A New Pair of Shoes
Signed with initials and dated 1866
Watercolour with bodycolour
12 ¾ x 9 inches

MYLES BIRKET FOSTER

Myles Birket Foster, RWS (1825-1899)

Myles Birket Foster was one of the most popular artists of the Victorian period, achieving success first as an illustrator and then as an exhibition watercolourist. In both disciplines, he conveyed a gentle naturalism through mastery of technique.

For a biography of Myles Birket Foster, please refer to *Chris Beetles Summer Show*, 2017, page 65.

28
Country Cottage
Signed with monogram
Watercolour with bodycolour
4 ½ x 6 ¾ inches

29

Highland Waterfall
Signed with monogram
Watercolour with bodycolour
6 ¾ x 10 inches
Exhibited: 'Winter Exhibition', Queen's Park Art Gallery,
City of Manchester, 1903, no 605

30
Rhubarb and Cauliflower
Indistinctly signed [Dering]
and dated 1890
Watercolour
10 ½ x 7 ¼ inches

HERCULES BRABAZON BRABAZON

Hercules Brabazon Brabazon, NEAC PS (1821-1906)

For much of his life, Hercules Brabazon Brabazon pleased himself as a gentleman traveller, producing luminous, loosely-handled watercolours of favourite paintings and places (including India, which he visited in 1870, 1875 and 1876). Admired by John Ruskin as an heir to J M W Turner, he joined the eminent critic on a sketching tour to northern France in 1880. Yet his startling modernity was probably recognised only in the 1890s, by a younger generation of artists, which included John Singer Sargent, Walter Sickert and Philip Wilson Steer.

Through their enthusiasm, he was elected a member of the New English Art Club in 1891, and held the first of a series of solo shows at the Goupil Gallery in the following year.

For a biography of Hercules Brabazon Brabazon, please refer to *Chris Beetles Summer Show*, 2016, page 36

31

Red Flowers in a Blue Vase
Signed
Watercolour with bodycolour and varnish
8 ¾ x 5 ¾ inches
Exhibited: 'Hercules Brabazon Brabazon (1821-1906) and the New English Art Club', Chris Beetles Gallery, London, October 1986, no 82

32

Study of Flowers
Signed with initials
Watercolour and pastel
9 ¾ x 7 inches

33
Richmond Castle, Yorkshire
Signed with initials
Watercolour and bodycolour on tinted paper
6 ¾ x 9 ½ inches

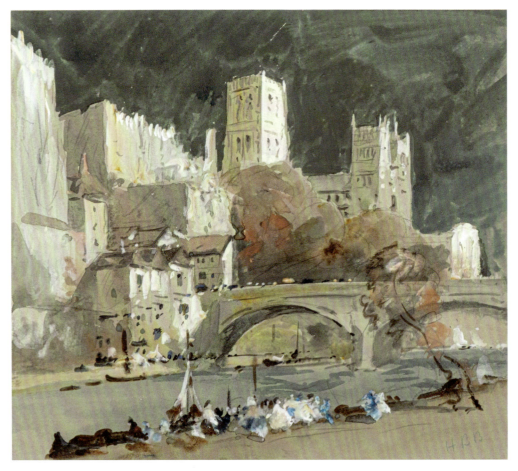

34
Durham
Signed with initials
Watercolour and bodycolour on tinted paper
9 x 10 ¼ inches
Provenance: John R Goodyear Collection
Exhibited: 'Hercules Brabazon Brabazon 1821-1906', Chris Beetles Gallery, London, 1989, no 59

35
Souvenir of Velázquez, Las Meninas (below)
Watercolour and bodycolour
13 x 10 inches

The figure in this study is María Agustina Sarmiento de Sotomayor, one of Las Meninas or 'ladies-in-waiting' in the picture of the same name by Velázquez. She offers a drink to the Infanta Margaret Theresa, who is the focal point of the painting.

Brabazon first visited Madrid in 1848, encountering the work of Velázquez at the Museo del Prado. Las Meninas has been part of the collection since the museums conception but was officially registered with this name in the 1843 catalogue, just a few years before Brabazon would paint this souvenir.

Due to its size and value the painting is never loaned, and the only time it left the Prado is during the evacuation in the last months of the Spanish Civil War. Therefore, we can be certain that Brabazon studied this important picture amongst works by Velázquez that influenced his own work.

36 (above)
The Fighting Temeraire
Signed with initials
Watercolour and bodycolour
4 ½ x 7 inches

After the oil by Joseph Mallord Turner, *The Fighting Temeraire, tugged to her last berth to be broken up*, painted in 1838 and exhibited at the Royal Academy in the following year.

37 (left)
Servant Girl. After Charles Robert Leslie
Signed with initials
Watercolour and bodycolour on tinted paper
7 x 3 ¼ inches
Provenance: John R Goodyear Collection
Exhibited: 'Hercules Brabazon Brabazon (1821-1906)', Chris Beetles Gallery, London, November-December 1982, no 285

HERCULES BRABAZON BRABAZON

38 (left)
Venice
Signed with initials
Watercolour
8 ¾ x 9 inches
Provenance: John R Goodyear Collection
Exhibited: 'Hercules Brabazon Brabazon
(1821-1906)', Chris Beetles Gallery, London,
November-December 1982, no 180
and catalogue front cover

39 (below)
Across the Lagoon, Venice
Signed with initials
Watercolour, bodycolour and pencil
on tinted paper
9 x 12 ¼ inches
Provenance: John R Goodyear Collection

ALFRED WILLIAM HUNT

Alfred William Hunt, VPRWS (1830-1896)

Though they came from very different social backgrounds, Alfred William Hunt may be compared to his friend, Albert Goodwin, as one of the leading landscape painters to follow the principles of John Ruskin. He achieved this by 'fusing the sweep and atmosphere of Turner with Pre-Raphaelite finish and compositional originality' (Scott Wilcox, 1996, page 24).

For a biography of Alfred William Hunt, please refer to *Chris Beetles Summer Show*, 2018, page 38.

40
Conwy Castle
Signed with initials and dated '56
Watercolour
10 x 15 inches
Exhibited: 'The Poetry of Truth. Alfred William Hunt and The Art of Landscape': Yale Center For British Art, September-December, 2004, & Ashmolean Museum, January-April, 2005, no 9

EDMUND GEORGE WARREN

Edmund George Warren, RI ROI (1834-1909)

Edmund George Warren was perhaps the best known of all Victorian watercolourists to specialise in arboreal landscapes and woodland scenes. He painted minutely detailed views of shady glades and the forest floor, and delighted in describing the effects of sunlight breaking through the canopy of leaves. He also enjoyed painting harvest scenes in the company of George Vicat Cole.

For a biography of Edmund George Warren, please refer to *Chris Beetles Summer Show*, 2021, page 110.

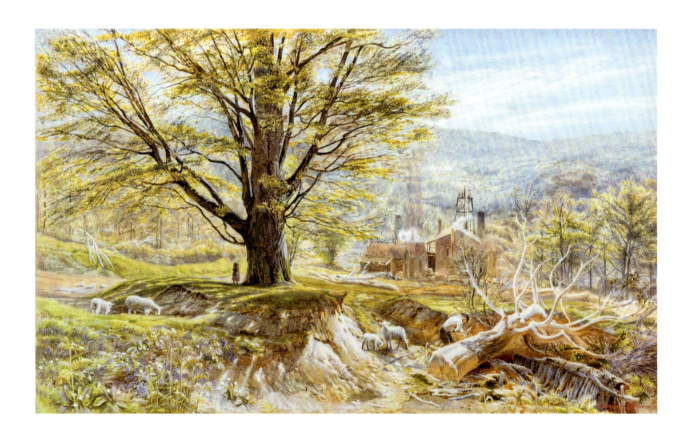

41
The Woodcutter
Signed and dated 1868
Watercolour
10 ½ x 18 inches

CONSTANCE FREDERICA GORDON-CUMMING

Constance Frederica Gordon-Cumming (1837-1924)

Constance Frederica Gordon-Cumming was one of the most intrepid and enterprising women travellers of the Victorian period, who also had the skill and industry to record her journeys in word and image. Encouraged by her many distinguished connections, during the height of the British Empire, she visited India, Ceylon and many of the countries of the Pacific Rim, between 1868 and 1880. The extent of her achievement is still in the process of evaluation.

For a biography of Constance Frederica Gordon-Cumming, please refer to *Chris Beetles Summer Show*, 2014, pages 13-14.

42

Luirang, Wreck of the Sampson
Signed with initials, inscribed with title and dated 1868
Watercolour with bodycolour
11 ¼ x 18 ¼ inches

HMS Sampson was a Royal Naval steam frigate, which was launched from Woolwich Dockyard in September 1844. She saw service in Lagos and the Black Sea and worked latterly in the 'Chinese Station' around Hong Kong. She sunk off China in 1864.

ARTHUR VEREY

Arthur Verey (1840-1915)

Though little is known about the life and career of Arthur Verey, he produced a body of work in watercolour and oil that recorded working class and rural women engaged in traditional occupations.

Thomas Arthur Verey was born in 1851 in Hanover Square, London, the son of Joseph Verey and his wife Sarah. The following year, his sister Clara was born. The census for 1861 records the family as living in the parish of St Mary Aldermanbury in the City of London. By 1881, the family had moved to Willesden, north London. In the census for that year, Arthur Verey's occupation is listed as an artist. He died in Willesden in July 1920.

43
**The Flower Girl,
St James's Square**
Signed
Watercolour with bodycolour
15 ¾ x 11 ¾ inches

EDITH MARTINEAU

Edith Martineau, ARWS (1842-1909)

Edith Martineau was a pioneering figure among artists of the Victorian period, in that she was one of the first women to be admitted to the Royal Academy Schools and one of the first to be elected an Associate of the Royal Society of Painters in

Water-Colours. She was also ambitious in the range of her subject matter, applying her admired precision of handling, to floral still life compositions, landscapes, rural genre scenes and portraits of children.

For a biography of Edith Martineau, please refer to *Chris Beetles Summer Show*, 2016, pages 20-21.

44
The Violinist
Signed and dated 1877
Watercolour with bodycolour
19 ¾ x 14 ¾ inches

ALBERT GOODWIN

Albert Frederick Goodwin, RWS RWA (1845-1932)

In synthesising the influences of J M W Turner and the Pre-Raphaelites, Albert Goodwin may be considered one of the most Ruskinian of Victorian landscape painters. Indeed, he was taken up by John Ruskin and, in 1872, given the opportunity to travel with him on an intensive tour of Italy and Switzerland. This set the pattern for many further and extensive travels. Like Ruskin, Goodwin responded to landscape with a religious fervour and understanding; but he interpreted it with greater eclecticism than did his mentor, even experimenting with the style of James McNeill Whistler, Ruskin's adversary in the field of aesthetics.

For a biography of Albert Goodwin, please refer to *Chris Beetles Summer Show*, 2014, page 26.

45

Chichester from the Bishop's Garden
Signed and inscribed with title
Enclosed within an ink border
Watercolour and bodycolour
10 x 14 ½ inches
Provenance: Matthew Biggar Walker;
Christie's, London, 9 March 1928, lot 77,
'The Collection of Matthew Biggar Walker'
Exhibited: 'A collection of oil paintings, water colour drawings etc. By Albert Goodwin, RWS, RWA. Lent by M B Walker Esq. City of Birmingham Museum and Art Gallery, 1926, no 56

Chichester Cathedral was originally consecrated in 1108 and evolved to its current form in 1400 when the spire, cloisters and bell tower were built. However in 1861 the tower and spire collapsed and Sir George Gilbert Scott oversaw the rebuilding. The cathedral was fully reopened five years later in 1866. The spire and tower in Goodwin's painting were therefore completed only a few decades before this work. The Bishop's Gardens, on the western end of the cathedral, were established as early as 1147-1148.

46
St Davids, S Wales
Signed and inscribed with title
Enclosed within an ink border
Ink with pencil and bodycolour on tinted paper
9 ½ x 11 ½ inches
Preliminary drawing for 'St. Davids', exhibited in the Royal
Society of Painters in Water-Colours, Winter 1889, no 343
and illustrated in *Albert Goodwin RWS, 1845-1932*, London:
Chris Beetles Ltd, 1986, Limited Edition of 1000, plate 38.

The ruins of St Davids Bishops Palace, Pembrokeshire, are
sited on the opposite bank of the river Alun (seen in the
foreground) to St Davids Cathedral. The original monastery
was established by St David in the 6th century and for the
next 400 years was subjected to regular attacks by Norse
raiders. In the 11th century the Normans undertook
extensive ecclesiastical building work including many defensive
walls. Successive bishops added to the Palace and the ruins
depicted are largely from the late 13th and 14th centuries.

47
Abingdon
Signed and inscribed with title
Watercolour, bodycolour and pencil on tinted paper
10 x 13 ¾ inches

48
Clovelly
Signed and inscribed with title
Ink and pencil on tinted paper
10 x 14 inches

This is the preliminary drawing
for the watercolour of the
same title from the Raymond
Gould Collection, painted in
1884 and later repainted in
1921.

49 (left)

Mortehoe, N Devon
Signed and inscribed with title
Enclosed within an ink border
Watercolour and bodycolour with ink
10 x 14 inches
Provenance: Matthew Biggar Walker
Exhibited: 'A collection of oil paintings, water colour drawings etc.
By Albert Goodwin, RWS, RWA. Lent by M B Walker Esq. City of
Birmingham Museum and Art Gallery, 1926, no 27 as
'Morte Hoe, N Devon'

Mortehoe, on the north coast of Devon is situated in a valley to the
east of the rocky peninsula of Morte Point. Whose dramatic rock
formations were not only the cause of many shipwrecks and featured
in several of Goodwin's watercolours. Here, the village of Mortehoe
catches the evening sunlight, with Morte Point in the distance.

50 (above)

Ilfracombe, Devon
Signed
Oil on board
12 ½ x 15 inches
Exhibited: Probably 'A collection of pictures and drawings of
imaginative landscape in Europe and Asia by Albert Goodwin, RWS',
Fine Art Society, London, March 1896, no 24 as 'High Street, Ilfracombe'

51

**The rising moon on Galley Hill,
Looking Towards St Leonards**
Signed, inscribed with title and dated
1921
Enclosed in a decorative border
Watercolour, bodycolour and oil with
pencil on tinted paper
10 x 14 inches

52

Hartland Quay
Signed with monogram and inscribed with title
Watercolour
8 ½ x 13 ¼ inches
Provenance: Matthew Biggar Walker;
Christie's, London, 9 March 1928, lot 40,
'The Collection of Matthew Biggar Walker';

Raymond Gould Collection
Exhibited: 'A Collection of Water-Colour Drawings of Many-Sided Nature by
Albert Goodwin, RWS', Fine Art Society, London, 1890, no 12;
A collection of oil paintings, water colour drawings etc. By Albert Goodwin, RWS,
RWA. Lent by M.B. Walker Esq', City of Birmingham Museum and Art Gallery,
1926, no 31

53
Beachy Head
Signed and inscribed with title
Pencil and chalk on tinted paper
10 ¾ x 15 inches
Exhibited: Possibly 'Watercolours and
Drawings by Albert Goodwin, RWS',
Walker Galleries, London, July 1961,
no 2 as 'A bit of Beachy Head, Sussex'

Preliminary drawing for *Beachy Head –
The Coastguard's Story*, 1908/9, which
was exhibited at The Fine Art Society,
London, 1908, no 23.

54
Dover
Signed, inscribed with title
and dated 1910
Watercolour
9 ½ x 13 ½ inches

55

A Distant View of Lincoln
Signed with monogram and dated 88
Watercolour
10 ¾ x 17 ¼ inches
Provenance: Peter Lord Collection
Literature: *Albert Goodwin RWS, 1845-1932*, London:
Chris Beetles, 1986, Limited Edition of 1000, Plate 35

Diary 1915, January 8th.

'Why do the days go so fast? It is the common daily remark that the week-ends knock against each other! I suppose we are all so fully occupied that that has something to do with the swift passing of the time. My day begins fairly regularly at 6.30, when I start by doing duty as family stoker! An interesting way of beginning the day at this dark season (black night till 7 a.m.) and to make the household fires is a very interesting way of beginning a cold, dark day. By 8 a.m. I am free to start painting. Should like (if I live) to do a book of drawings on our cathedrals at night. I have done them by day and have thought how wonderful, in their mystery, they show in the semi-darkness; the great west front of Lincoln, seeming to run right up into the stars! This kind of subject might be done or rather suggested in small drawings, which would be quite unsuitable for larger: for the darkness of tone of these make them impossible for pictures that are to be hung up. They would look like a mere black hole in the wall, and if they were glazed (as all water-colours are) you would mostly see only your own reflection in the glass! If done for a book, can be carried to the light and so can be understood and seen and enjoyed.'

56
Sunset
Signed, inscribed with title and dated 'July 14 1915'
Watercolour and bodycolour on tinted paper
13 x 20 inches

Diary, 1918, June 26th

'... though a golden sunset is a golden splendour to me, yet it is much more so when the dark clouds are in it. This may be partly morbid on my part, I daresay it is, but it is very much to the front, and a cloudless sky is to me simply uninteresting, and I do not seem to want to paint it, save sometimes to use it as a background for some earthly scene where the earthly part is the real subject of interest.'

57
A Sussex road
Westham by Pevensey
Signed, inscribed with title and dated 1918/19
Watercolour with bodycolour and ink
12 x 19 ½ inches

58

Canterbury Cathedral
Signed, inscribed 'Canterbury' and dated 1901
Watercolour with ink
10 ¾ x 14 ½ inches
Exhibited: Probably 'Sunset and Colour from East and West Drawings by Albert Goodwin, RWS',
Robert Dunthorne's The Rembrandt Head Gallery, London, 1912, no 12

59
Cambridge Backs, King's Chapel
Signed, inscribed with title and dated 1919
Watercolour
10 x 14 ¾ inches

Diary, 1913, November 3rd, Cambridge.

'Glad to be back here and with a St. Martin's summer. The sight of the "backs" has been one to rejoice over: never have I seen colour more resplendent. Two days spent in trying to get some of it have been spent in comfort instead of purgatory! for midges – if the weather is mild enough – make the doing of these subjects torture, otherwise the nip of the early frost, made sitting out of doors (for old bones) a precarious kind of matter; but midges this time have, I suppose, gone to an early grave, for they are not! To me a midge is worse than twenty mosquitoes!'

60

King's Parade, Cambridge
Signed, inscribed with title and dated 1913
Watercolour with ink
9 ¾ x 13 ¾ inches
Exhibited: 'Water-Colour Drawings and Paintings by
Albert Goodwin, RWS', Leggatt Brothers Gallery, London, 1912, no 59

61
Westminster
Signed, inscribed with title and dated 97
Watercolour with bodycolour and ink
10 x 14 ½ inches

62
Westminster, Sunset Through the Smoke
Signed, inscribed with title and dated 1913
Watercolour and bodycolour
12 ¼ x 19 ¾ inches

63
Fribourg, Suisse
Signed, inscribed
with title and
dated 1900
Watercolour
10 x 14 inches

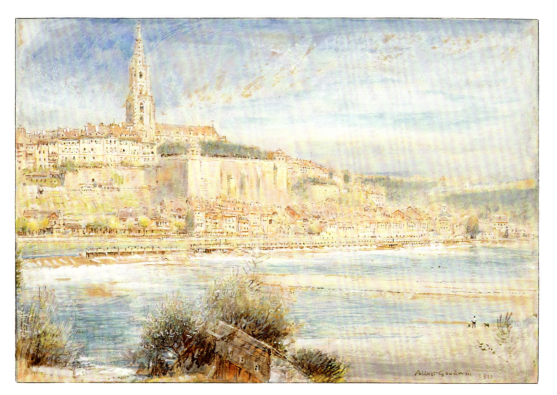

64
Berne
Signed, inscribed
with title
and dated 1911
Watercolour and
bodycolour
9 ¾ x 14 ¾ inches
Exhibited: Probably
'Water-Colour
Drawings and
Paintings by Albert
Goodwin, RWS',
Leggatt Brothers
Gallery, London,
1912, no 37

65

Ouchy, Lausanne
Signed, inscribed with title and
dated 88
Watercolour and bodycolour
with pencil
10 ½ x 13 ½ inches
Exhibited: 'Drawings and Pictures
by Albert Goodwin, RWS',
Leggatt Brothers Gallery,
London, 1919, no 24

66

Landeck
Signed, inscribed
with title and
dated 1912
Signed below mount
Watercolour and
bodycolour
10 x 15 inches

67

Torre Anuniciata & Vesuvius
Signed and inscribed with title
Ink and pencil on tinted paper
6 ¾ x 9 ¾ inches
Exhibited: Probably 'Drawings and
Pictures by Albert Goodwin,
RWS', Leggatt Brothers Gallery,
London, 1908, no 68

Sketches of figures on reverse

68

**Mont Rosa from
Como's Hills**
Signed and inscribed with title
Watercolour and bodycolour
11 x 14 ½ inches

69

Circe and the Swine
Signed and inscribed with title
Inscribed 'The house of the Chambers
of Death' on border
Enclosed within an ink border
Watercolour with bodycolour
8 ¼ x 10 ¾ inches

70

The House of Circe
'Thou hast given them
a drink of the dry wine'
Signed, inscribed with title and dated
1919
Watercolour with bodycolour
13 ½ x 18 inches
Provenance: Matthew Biggar Walker;
Christie's, London, 9 March 1928,
lot 14, 'The Collection of
Matthew Biggar Walker'
Exhibited: Royal Society of Painters in
Water-Colours, Summer 1919,
no 7, as 'The House of the Circe'

HELEN ALLINGHAM

Helen Mary Elizabeth Allingham
(née Paterson), RWS (1848-1926)

**One of the most successful women
artists of the Victorian age,
Helen Allingham produced archetypal
watercolour images of cottages
and gardens.**

For a biography of Helen Allingham, please
refer to *Chris Beetles Summer Show*, 2016,
page 18.

71
Portrait of a young girl
Signed
Watercolour
4 ¾ x 4 ¾ inches

72
Coming Through
Signed
Watercolour
8 ¼ x 6 ¼ inches

The Fields in May

What can better please,
When your mind is well at ease,
Than a walk among the green fields in May?
To see the verdure new,
And to hear the loud cuckoo,
While sunshine makes the whole world gay:

When the butterfly so brightly
On his journey dances lightly,
And the bee goes by with business-like hum;
When the fragrant breeze and soft
Stirs the shining clouds aloft,
And the children's hair, as laughingly
they come:

When the grass is full of flowers,
And the hedge is full of bowers,
And the finch and the linnet piping clear,
Where the branches throw their shadows
On a footway through the meadows,
With a brook among the cresses
winding near.

Any pair of lovers walking
On this footway in sweet talking,
Sweeter silence, often linger and delay,
For the path, not very wide,
Brings them closer, side by side,
Moving gently through the happy fields
of May:

Till they rest themselves awhile
At the elm-o'ershaded stile,
When stars begin to tremble in the blue,
Just to hear a nightingale,
Near our village in the vale,
To his sweetheart singing carols fond
and true:

Evening wind, and brooklet's flow,
Softly whisper as they go,
Every star throbs with tenderness above;
Tender lips are sure to meet,
Heart to heart must warmly beat,
When the earth is fall and heaven is full
of love.

Oh, I would the song I sing
Might to me a sweetheart bring,
For companion through the green fields
of May!
She should nestle in my heart,
And we never more should part,
While the summers and the winters
roll'd away.

73
The Fields in May
Signed
Watercolour and ink
12 ½ x 10 inches

This watercolour illustrates a poem in a book by her husband,
William Allingham, *Flower Pieces and Other Poems*, London: Longman,
Green & Co, 1893, pages 50-51

JAMES THOMAS WATTS

James Thomas Watts, RBSA, RCamA (1853-1930)

As a follower of John Ruskin and the paintings of the Pre-Raphaelites, James Thomas Watts dedicated himself to painting the truth of nature, particularly through woodland landscapes. Best known for this narrow range of subject matter, he meticulously explored these scenes through the different seasons and times of day, in order to develop subtleties of light that produced astonishingly atmospheric works.

For a biography of James Thomas Watts, please refer to page 142.

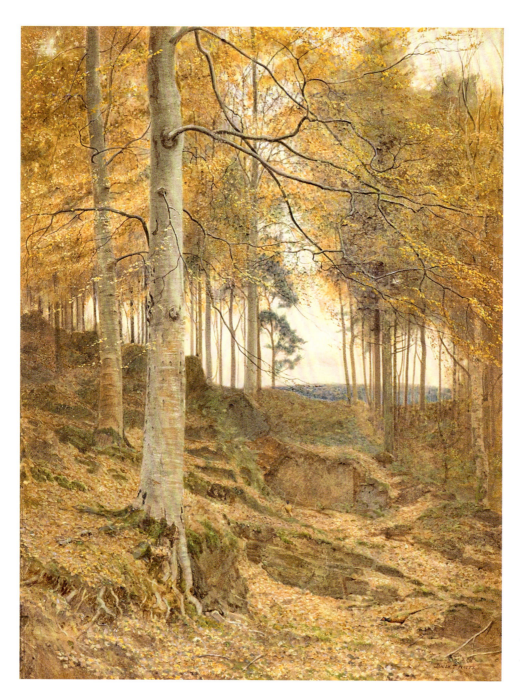

74
A Sussex Wood
Signed
Watercolour and bodycolour
21 x 16 ¼ inches

Chris Beetles Gallery rekindled interest in the work of J T Watts from the 1980s and over twenty years curated a significant group of eighteen watercolours for the prominent watercolour collector David Fuller. Further interest was generated by the auction of the Fuller Collection of Victorian Landscape Watercolours at Christie's London in April 2000, when record prices were achieved and significant lots were acquired by the Metropolitan Museum of Art, New York.

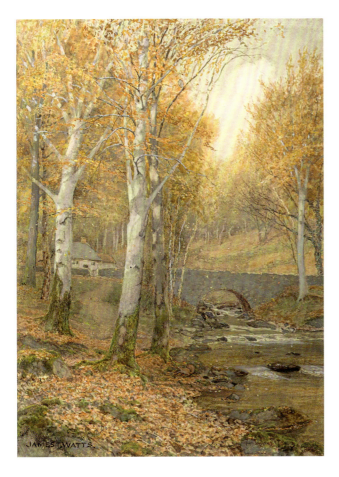

75
A Little Welsh Stream in Autumn
Signed
Watercolour
14 x 10 inches

76
Autumn Among Birch Trees
Signed
Watercolour
13 ¾ x 9 ½ inches

WALTER TYNDALE

Walter Frederick Roope Tyndale, RBC RI (1855-1943)

Walter Tyndale was one of the most popular and influential topographical watercolourists working at the turn of the century. He was also one of the first to benefit from the printing revolution of 1901 when his publishers, A & C Black, pioneered the use of three colour half-tone plates. The ensuing publishing boom led to a wealth of commissions for Tyndale for illustrated travel books, which took him from the Wessex countryside to Europe and the Far East.

For a biography of Walter Tyndale, please refer to *Chris Beetles Summer Show*, 2021, page 112.

77
Saracens, Surrey
Signed
Watercolour
10 ¼ x 14 inches

Saracens, Surrey

The house has been identified from images in Walter Tyndale's personal scrapbooks.

'Saracens', near Woking in Surrey and originally known as 'Saracen's Lair', was designed in 1901 by architect William Frederick Unsworth. Created for solicitor William Harrison in the arts and crafts style, Unsworth incorporated the medieval features that so inspired him, including the remarkable half-timbered tower reminiscent of the architecture in the Nuremberg region of Germany. A friend of Walter Tyndale, Unsworth also designed Tyndale's own house, 'Broad Dene' in Haslemere, Surrey.

Diary 1904

'During May 1904 I stayed at "Saracens", the house built by Unsworth for Mr Harrison brother of Frederick Harrison.'

78
Saracens from the Garden
Signed and dated 1904
Watercolour on board
10 x 13 ¼ inches

79
Littlecroft, Emery Down, home of Morton Kelsall Peto, 1886-1913
Signed
Inscribed 'Littlecroft, Lyndhurst', 'built by Ernest George for Mr Morton Peto' and on reverse
Watercolour on board
9 x 7 inches
Illustrated: Horace G Hutchinson, *The New Forest*, London: Methuen & Co, 1906, facing page 186, 'Littlecroft, Lyndhurst'

Littlecroft, Emery Down, home of Morton Kelsall Peto, 1886-1913

Morton Kelsall Peto was the son of Sir Morton Peto the renowned 19th century civil engineer. The Architect, Sir Ernest George RA also worked in partnership with Harold Peto, Kelsall Peto's younger brother.

'Littlecroft is a house and studio now building in the New Forest for Mr. Morton K. Peto. The external quarterings is of oak with parquet filling-in. The slope of the ground is taken advantage of so that an extra room is obtained in the height of the main gable, a boudoir being arranged on the first landing and above the porch. The oak staircase is worked in a square space behind posts and arches and can be screened by curtains from the hall, which latter is arranged to form an additional room to the house. The studio has an open roof and gallery and one end. The dining-room has an ingle behind an oak arch; overhead the beams are shown and a ceiling of wood panel with mitred mouldings.'

The Building News, 1 November 1884

80

Haslemere

Signed and dated 89
Watercolour with
bodycolour
6 ¾ x 9 ½ inches

Walter Tyndale lived in
Haselmere from the end
of the 1880s, soon after
his marriage to Evelyn
Barnard. In 1900 he
commissioned the Arts
and Crafts architect,
William Frederick
Unsworth, to design his
family home in Hill Road.
Tyndale also painted
another of Unsworth's
houses, 'Saracen's Lair'
near Woking at the same
time (see X and X).

81

**Summer Afternoon
on the Lawn, Surrey**

Signed and dated 96
Watercolour
9 ½ x 13 ¾ inches

82

The Cottage in the Wood, Shottermill
Signed
Inscribed with title on reverse
Watercolour
14 x 10 inches
Exhibited: Dowdeswell & Dowdeswells, London, no 26

At the turn of the last century, Shottermill was still an
independent village, only two miles from Tyndale's house,
'Broad Dene', in Haslemere.

83

Summer in Surrey, the Garden Steps
Signed and dated 93
Watercolour
9 ¼ x 6 ¼ inches

Shrewsbury
Signed
Watercolour
11 ½ x 9 ¼ inches

Shrewsbury

Joseph (Lewis) Della Porta was from a family of shopkeepers, originally from Northern Italy. Joseph Della Porta Snr settled in Shrewsbury and in 1857 established a small shop on Princess Street. The shop initially sold hardware and then diversified into furniture, household goods and clothing. As the business became more successful it expanded into adjoining premises, including Lloyds Mansion on the corner of Princess Street and The Square. By 1904 it was an established and thriving department store and in 1982 the business was sold to House of Fraser.

Lloyd's Mansion (as seen here) was built in 1570 by David Lloyd, a successful draper and local bailiff. It is considered to be the first house built in the Shrewsbury decorated timber frame style. It was demolished in the 1930s with the intention of being rebuilt near the castle but sadly, it never happened. A gable end of the mansion with its decorated carvings is on display in the Shrewsbury Museum and Art Gallery. Della Porta was a keen amateur photographer and in the late 1880s took extensive photographs of the local shop keepers, these are now preserved in the Shropshire Archives.

**Blackmore Vale,
from Shaftesbury
A scene in
*Jude the Obscure***
Signed
Inscribed with title
on reverse
Watercolour with
bodycolour
6 ¼ x 9 ¼ inches
Illustrated: Clive Holland and
Walter Tyndale, *Wessex*,
London: A & C Black, 1906,
facing page 120, plate 27

Blackmore Vale, from Shaftesbury. A scene in *Jude the Obscure*

'The road from Sherborne to Shaftesbury passes through sixteen miles of some of the prettiest scenery in Wessex, and crosses the famous Blackmore Vale midway between the two towns. Known formerly as the White Hart Forest, this fertile and secluded valley, through which the little river Cale flows to meet the Stour, with its old-world ways and rich pasture, is a spot, still little known to strangers, though frequented by artists, well worthy of a visit from those who appreciate rural and idyllic life.'
Clive Holland and Walter Tyndale, Wessex, page 118

86

Vinney Ridge
Signed
Inscribed '3 miles from Lyndhurst
on Christchurch road' on
original backboard
Watercolour
7 x 9 inches
Illustrated: Horace G Hutchinson,
The New Forest, London: Methuen
& Co, 1906, facing page 256

The Vinney Ridge Inclosure is
south west of Lyndhurst in the
Brinken Wood and consists of an
area of waterlogged forest,
enclosed by exotic conifers
which were planted in 1859.

87

The Gipsy Camp near the Kennels Between Lyndhurst & Minstead
Signed
Inscribed with title on original backboard
Watercolour
7 ¼ x 9 ½ inches
Illustrated: Horace G Hutchinson, *The New Forest*, London: Methuen & Co, 1906, facing page 204;
Also reproduced as a postcard

'On the whole, considering their mode of life and freedom from restraint, the gypsies of the New Forest
appear to behave as very well-conducted citizens towards those with whom they throw in their nomadic lot.'
Horace G Hutchinson, *The New Forest*, page 209

88
Beaulieu, Lyndhurst
Signed
Watercolour
7 x 9 ¼ inches
Illustrated: Horace G Hutchinson, *The New Forest*, London: Methuen & Co, 1906, facing page 68

'... there are several ways of approaching Beaulieu, but perhaps none is more pleasant than across Beaulieu Heath, a stretch of about three miles from Boldre. Southward lies the cultivated and rich valley land, northward and at your back the forest, and you traverse a wild and picturesque heath that might well belong to Scotland, instead of to the southernmost corner of England.'
Horace G Hutchinson, *The New Forest*, page 127-8

89

A Gravel Pit Head at Royden

Signed
Inscribed with title on reverse
Watercolour on board
9 x 7 inches
Illustrated: Horace G Hutchinson, *The New Forest*, London:
Methuen & Co, 1906, facing page 24;
Published as a postcard, circa 1904

'Royden Common, to the south, has the beauty that belongs to a
heather-clad country, with green walks diversifying the brown
purples of the heath. Here you begin to get more open and extended
views towards the south and the sea and the Isle of Wight.'
Horace G Hutchinson, *The New Forest*, page 123

90

Bell Heather on Setley Plain

Signed
Inscribed with title on original backboard
Watercolour
7 x 9 inches
Illustrated: Horace G Hutchinson, *The New Forest*, London:
Methuen & Co, 1906, facing page 276

'The plains and heaths are beautiful, in the proper season, with the
three kinds of heather, the bell heather being in especial luxuriance
in this mild southerly climate, and change their colouring at different
times with all the variety of hue that the bracken and the heather
can assume.'
Horace G Hutchinson, *The New Forest*, page 101

91

Cottage at Brading, Isle of Wight
Signed
Inscribed with title on original label on backboard
Watercolour
9 ¼ x 6 ½ inches
Exhibited: Frost & Reed, London, 7 May 1936, no 2113

92

The Retro-Choir, Winchester Cathedral, with the Chantries of Cardinal Beaufort and Bishop Waynflete
Signed
Watercolour
8 ½ x 11 inches
Illustrated: Clive Holland and Walter Tyndale, *Wessex*, London: A & C Black, 1906, facing page 226, plate 56

Winchester cathedral was built between 1079-1532. Its very long (558 feet) nave is in the Perpendicular Gothic style with a Norman tower and transepts.

Tyndale has painted looking east through the Early English retrochoir towards the Lady Chapel with the Chantries of Bishops Waynflete and Beaufort on either side.

'There are four interesting chantries close by that of Waynflete, dating from the fifteenth century, and distinguished for its beautiful canopy; and those of Cardinal Beaufort, of rather earlier date, Bishop Gardiner, which contains the tombstone of King Edmund, and Bishop Fox, dating from the early part of the sixteenth century.' Clive Holland and Walter Tyndale, *Wessex*, page 225

93
Wessex Homestead
Signed and dated 93
Watercolour
6 ¼ x 9 ¼ inches

Weymouth Bay

'Westward from Swanage about twenty-two miles by water, and south-west from Dorchester over the ridge of chalk downs towards the sea, reached by good roads in the past, and nowadays easily accessible also by rail, Weymouth lies in the curve of one of the finest bays on the south coast ...'
Clive Holland and Walter Tyndale, *Wessex*, page 72

94
Weymouth Bay
Signed and dated 95
Watercolour
6 ½ x 9 ½ inches
Illustrated: Similar to
Clive Holland and
Walter Tyndale,
Wessex, London:
A & C Black, 1906,
facing page 82,
'Portland from the
Northern Shore of
Weymouth Bay.
"The Isle of Slinger"
of the Novels'

ETHEL ATCHERLEY

Ethel Atcherley (1864-1905)

Known primarily as a landscape artist, depicting rustic scenes in watercolour and oil, Ethel Atcherley was also a talented sculptor, exhibiting work in this medium in her native Manchester. Before her premature death at the age of 41, she saw her works displayed at the Royal Academy of Arts, Manchester Academy of Fine Arts and the Royal Society of British Artists.

For a biography of Ethel Atcherley, please refer to page 142.

95
The Sculptor's Studio
Signed
Watercolour
16 x 23 inches
Provenance: Edward McLaughlin Collection

TOM CLOUGH

Tom Clough, RCA (1867-1943)

Tom Clough was born on 12 July 1867 in Bolton, Greater Manchester.

He began a career in lithographic printing before briefly setting up a drapery business after his father, who worked as a weaver. However, from these early endeavours he 'spent his first sixpence on paint' and started exhibiting paintings in his early twenties. By the age of 24 he was working full-time as a landscape artist in Bolton.

Tom Clough first gained attention when his painting *The Gorsy Marsh* was shown in the Royal Academy Summer Exhibition in 1894 (no 447). In total ten of his pictures were shown in the Summer Exhibitions at the Royal Academy between 1894 and 1919.

In 1895 he moved to North Wales with his wife Caroline, where they would settle and have two children.

Once elected a member of the Royal Cambrian Academy, Tom Clough exhibited works for major societies across London and Birmingham, as well as at Manchester City Art Gallery and The Walker Gallery, Liverpool. Many of his paintings depicted where he lived and the surrounding areas. Although, he often travelled further afield to paint Cornwall, Italy and France.

According to his obituary in the *North Wales Weekly News*, 'he always declared that he owed most of his knowledge to an untiring study of nature'. Tom Clough died in Llandudno, North Wales in 1943.

96
Pentre Wood. Bettws-y-coed
Signed
Watercolour
21 x 29 inches

ALBERTO PISA

Alberto Pisa (1864-1936)

Alberto Pisa was an Italian watercolourist and landscape artist best known as a painter of architectural and genre scenes of Italian towns. His asscociation with the Macchiaioli movement influenced his commitment throughout his career to capturing beauty in nature and urban scenes through subtleties of light and shade.

For a biography of Alberto Pisa, please refer to page 143.

97
The Royal Exchange
Signed
Watercolour with bodycolour
12 ¾ x 16 ¾ inches

CARLO PELLEGRINI

Carlo Giovanni Battista Pellegrini (1866-1937

The Italian-born Carlo Pellegrini was known as a talented painter in oil and tempera of snowy landscape scenes in his native northern Italy. A move to the Swiss Alps saw Pellegrini develop into a popular illustrator of postcards and posters extolling the excitement of winter sports such as skiing and ice skating. His reputation as an admired painter of sporting scenes led him to participate in the 1912 Olympic Games in Stockholm, where he became the first man to win an Olympic Gold Medal for Painting.

For a biography of Carlo Pellegrini, please refer to page 144.

98
Milan Cathedral
Signed
Oil on canvas
23 ¼ x 47 inches

EDWARD HANDLEY-READ

Edward Harry Handley-Read, MBE RBA (1870-1935)

Establishing himself as a wide-ranging artist and illustrator during the 1890s, Edward Handley-Read produced pioneering and powerful images of the front line during the First World War.

For a biography of Edward Handley-Read, please refer to pages 144-145.

99

Battle of Ypres
Signed, inscribed with title and dated 1919
Pastel on tinted paper
18 x 23 inches

100
Peronne
Signed and inscribed with title
Charcoal and watercolour
19 x 25 inches

Peronne

Peronne is a small town close to where the Battles of the Somme took place during the First World War. This picture shows an angle of the ruined main square during the German occupation of the town between 1914 and 1917. The town hall bears a sign reading 'Nicht ärgern nur wundern!' which translates as 'Don't be angry only marvel!' The town was liberated by Australian troops in 1918, and today the sign is in the collection of the History Museum in Peronne.

FRANK BRANGWYN

Sir Frank William Brangwyn (1867-1956)

Frank Brangwyn fulfilled his own belief, stated in 1934, that an artist 'must be able to turn his hand to everything, for his mission is to decorate life'. Though modest about his own achievements, he was ambitious in the range and scale of his art, creating large-scale murals, oils and watercolours, illustrations and prints, ceramics, furniture, stained-glass and textiles, in emulation of traditional workshop practice. He was particularly successful at arranging large numbers of figures into complex compositions that vary in mood from impassioned to celebratory.

For a biography of Sir Frank Brangwyn, please refer to *Chris Beetles Summer Show*, 2001, page 48.

101
Albi Cathedral
Signed with initials
Watercolour and bodycolour
19 ½ x 23 ½ inches
Provenance: Cecil Arthur Hunt Collection

CECIL ARTHUR HUNT

Cecil Arthur Hunt, VPRWS RBA (1873-1965)

Once elected a full member of the Royal Society of Painters in Water-Colours in 1925, Cecil Arthur Hunt retired from his career as a barrister and turned his serious pastime of painting into a profession. While he had first established himself as a painter of mountains, especially the Alps and the Dolomites, he soon proved himself a master of a great variety of topographies. The impressive, often stark, effects that he achieved rival those associated with his friend and mentor, Frank Brangwyn.

For a biography of Cecil Arthur Hunt, please refer to page 145.

102
Still Life of Flowers
Signed twice [faint signature inverted at top]
Bodycolour with watercolour
11 x 8 ¼ inches

103
China Clay – South Devon
Signed twice
Inscribed with title on reverse
Watercolour with bodycolour
9 x 13 ½ inches
Exhibited: 'Cecil Arthur Hunt VPRWS RBA', Chris Beetles Gallery, London, October 1996, no 27; 'Recording Britain: The Twentieth Century Landscape', Chris Beetles Gallery, London, February 2008, no 81

Lee Moor China Clay

Lee Moor is in the south west corner of Dartmoor, only 25 miles from Hunt's home in Manaton. His sketchbooks (sb13-42, 1924-1956) are full of drawings of the surreal luminous whites of the quarry which Hunt enjoyed placing against the natural backdrop of the Dartmoor hills.

104
Lee Moor China Clay – South Devon
Signed
Signed and inscribed with title on reverse
Watercolour, bodycolour and crayon
11 x 15 inches
Exhibited: 'Cecil Arthur Hunt VPRWS RBA', Chris Beetles Gallery, London October 1996, no 32

105

The Slag Heap, Black Country

Signed

Signed and inscribed with title on reverse

Watercolour with bodycolour

9 ¾ x 13 inches

Exhibited: 'Retrospective', Royal Society
of Painters in Water-Colours, May 1966,
additional work unnumbered;
'Cecil Arthur Hunt VPRWS RBA',
Chris Beetles Gallery, London,
October 1996, no 6;
'Recording Britain: The Twentieth
Century Landscape', Chris Beetles
Gallery, London, February 2008, no 80

The industrial environment juxtaposed
with the echoing undulations of the
surrounding natural landscape was a
relationship that appealed to Hunt.
The drama, billowing smoke and the
rigid additions of fence posts or
industrial buildings enabled Hunt to
fully utilise his renowned technique.
Where, he scraped through an overlay
of viscous gouache, often with the end
of a paintbrush, to reveal the layers of
watercolour beneath. Therefore, giving
depth and defining the highlights and
details.

106

**Dorothea Quarry,
Pen Y Groes**

Signed

Inscribed with title
on reverse

Watercolour and
bodycolour

10 ½ x 14 ¼ inches

Exhibited: Royal
Society of Painters in
Water-Colours,
Winter 1926, no 47,
bought by
L T Glasson;

In 1926 Hunt toured
Wales, concentrating
on the area around
Snowdon where the
impressive, theatrical
qualities of the slate
quarries inspired him
to paint.

107
Precipice and Pine
Signed
Inscribed with title on original backboard
Watercolour and bodycolour
14 ¾ x 21 ¾ inches
Exhibited: Royal Society of Painters in Water-Colours, Spring 1954,
no 107, as 'Precipice and Pine, Rosenlau'

A keen member of the Alpine Club, Hunt frequently visited the Alps and Dolomites in pursuit of dramatic subjects for his paintings as well as challenging walks and climbs. In June and July 1953, Hunt and his wife Phyllis stayed at the Royal Hotel in Lucerne, travelling and sketching the surrounding area on extended day trips by car and steamer. Rosenlaui lies above Meiringen in the Bernese Oberland, and is only a mile from the Reichenbach falls, the scene of the fatal struggle between Sherlock Holmes and Moriarty.

108

Hanging Monastery, Meteora, Thessaly
Signed and inscribed with title on reverse
Watercolour
22 x 30 inches
Illustrated: *The Illustrated London News,* 29 June 1935
Exhibited: Royal Society of Painters in Water-colours, Winter 1931, no 67;
'Cecil Arthur Hunt VPRWS RBA', Chris Beetles Gallery, London, October 1996, no 81

Hunt first came across the hanging monasteries of Meteora in Greece on a tour with his friend and fellow artist, Curtis Green RA and his wife, in May 1931. He sketched several variations in his sketchbook [30], one of which he worked up to complete this painting. The medium format sketchbook was inscribed in the front: 'With Curtis Green RA & Mrs G. Venice in a few days then steamer to Athens via Corinth Canal. Voyage in Greece & car to hanging monasteries of Meteora etc etc back from Brindisi up east coast of Italy to Stresa on L. Maggiore. See also book of photos and picture postcards.'

CECIL ARTHUR HUNT

109
Above Wengen, Switzerland
Signed
Watercolour with bodycolour
9 x 13 inches

Hunt visited Wengen in 1931 (in the same trip as the Hanging Monasty, Meteora, Thessaly, [**108**]) and in the sketchbook of that year, there is a photograph of his wife, Phyllis and his son, Vernon at a fancy dress party in Wengen. A keen climber and member of the Alpine Club, Hunt was inspired by the imposing scenery and clarity of light at Wengen and also sketched Lauterbrunnen, Thun and Spiez, the same areas that Albert Goodwin had been similarly inspired to paint a few decades earlier. [Sketchbook 31]

Les Baux

Hunt made sketches of the severe and majestic Les Baux in Provence during a motoring tour of southern France in 1921, (Sketchbook 4).

Les Baux-de-Provence is in the Alpilles mountains, north of Arles, in Southern France. Perched atop a 245m rocky outcrop, the medieval Château des Baux-de-Provence, was a built as stronghold during a period of turbulent military history. The powerful atmosphere of this severe subject is further enhanced by the onset of a tempestuous storm.

110
Les Baux
Signed and inscribed with title on reverse
Watercolour and bodycolour
10 ¾ x 14 ½ inches
Exhibited: Possibly the work exhibited at Royal Glasgow Institute of the Fine Arts, 1925, no 453 as 'Les Baux, Provence' [£31];
'Cecil Arthur Hunt VPRWS RBA', Chris Beetles Gallery, London, October 1996, no 146

WILLIAM WALCOT

William F Walcot,
RBA RE (1874-1943)

**Working as a painter and
printmaker, William Walcot
became the most celebrated
architectural artist in England
during the 1920s and 30s.**

For a biography of William Walcot,
please refer to *Chris Beetles Summer Show*,
2014, pages 42-43.

111
**Figures under the portico of the
National Gallery,
with St Martin-in-the-Fields beyond**
Watercolour with ink
23 ¼ x 11 ¾ inches

FREDERICK LANDSEER MAUR GRIGGS

Frederick Landseer Maur Griggs, RA RE (1876-1938)

Frederick Landseer Maur Griggs was considered to be one of the finest and most respected etchers of his generation. Influenced as a young man by the work of Samuel Palmer, he created stunning and dramatic compositions of gothic buildings and haunting landscapes, guided by his religious upbringing and training as an architectural draughtsman.

For a biography of Frederick Maur Landseer Griggs, please refer to page 146.

112
The Almonry
Signed in pencil
Inscribed on reverse
'Trial proof no 3, only 4 in this state'
Etching
10 x 6 ¾ inches
Illustrated: Malcolm C Salaman,
Modern Masters of Etching, F L Griggs,
London: The Studio, 1926, plate XII
Literature: Malcolm C Salaman
(editor), *Fine Prints of the Year*,
London: Halton & Truscott Smith,
vol 3, 1925, plate 22,
Francis Adams Comstock, *A Gothic
Vision: F.L. Griggs And His Work*,
Boston: Boston Public Library and
Ashmolean Museum Oxford, 1966,
catalogue raisonné no 34

Third state, in which there were four
proofs (fifth state had 82 impressions)

DAISY RADCLIFFE BERESFORD

Daisy Radcliffe Beresford (1879-1939)

Daisy Radcliffe Beresford (née Clague) studied at Heatherley's School of Art and the Royal Academy Schools where she won three silver and two bronze medals. She specialised in portraits, landscapes and interiors and exhibited regularly from 1904-1938, including the Royal Academy where she exhibited 12 paintings. She married Frank Ernest Beresford in 1910, a fellow student at the RA Schools and an official war artist. They had two daughters, Averil and also Vivian who later became the sculptor Vivian Bartholomew.

The Beresfords lived at 28 Grove End Road, St John's Wood, near the Reid-Dicks at 16 Maida Vale, where she painted, the sculptor, Sir William Reid-Dick's younger daughter Ann.

The Reid-Dick family, with Ann on the left

Ann's Tune

Sir William Reid Dick RA was a Scottish Sculptor renowned for his monumental and portrait sculpture. He was knighted in 1935 by King George V and was Sculptor in Ordinary from 1938 until his death in 1961. He lived with his wife, Catherine and their three children in Maida Vale. This painting shows Ann, his youngest daughter, playing the piano in their home at 16 Maida Vale. Her father's statue, *Sling Boy*, sits on the piano and a portrait of Lady Reid-Dick hangs behind.

113

Ann's Tune
Signed and dated 1932
Signed, inscribed with title, 'No 2' and '28 Grove End Road, St John's Wood, NW8' on reverse
Oil on board
13 ¾ x 10 inches
Provenance: Sir William Reid Dick RA and thence by descent to his daughter, Ann Benton and thence by descent to her children

STANLEY ANDERSON

Alfred Charles Stanley Anderson, RA RE (1884-1966)

The printmaker and painter, Stanley Anderson, was a major figure in the revival of line engraving between the wars. Though a long career allowed for a diverse range of subjects, his skill was displayed particularly well in a series of prints of farm workers and rural craftsmen.

For a biography of Stanley Anderson, please refer to *Chris Beetles Summer Show*, 2017, page 112.

114
The Rick Yard
Signed
Watercolour
8 x 10 ¾ inches

RANDOLPH SCHWABE

Randolph Schwabe, RWS LG NEAC (1885-1948)

A clear eye and sure hand enabled Randolph Schwabe to produce drawings, etchings and lithographs of consistent clarity and strength. Trained at the Slade School of Fine Art, he would return there to become an influential Principal and Professor. He also held a significant position as an Official War Artist in both world wars. Though he is best remembered for his attentive, absorbing images of buildings and landscapes, his subjects included figures and still life compositions, and he also produced illustrations and designs for the theatre.

For a biography of Randolph Schwabe, please refer to *Chris Beetles Summer Show*, 2017, pages 115-116.

The Bandstand, Dover

Badly damaged during WW1, Schwabe depicts the recently renovated bandstand in Granville Gardens, on the sea front at Dover. During the interwar period the bandstand, gardens and library became a popular venue but this was sadly short-lived when, during the second world war, a barrage balloon was erected in the gardens and the area became an obvious target for enemy aircraft. As a result, the Grand Hotel (on the right) and the sweeping Camden Crescent (to the left) were badly damaged on multiple occasions. The area was then redeveloped in the late 1950s, Granville Gardens were re-laid as public gardens but without a bandstand.

115
The Bandstand, Dover
Signed and dated 1924
Watercolour and pencil with bodycolour
12 ½ x 15 ½ inches

116 (left)
Albany, Burlington Street, W1
Signed and dated 1928
Ink and watercolour
16 ¼ x 12 inches

117 (below, left)
Church Row, Hampstead
Signed with initials, inscribed with title and dated 1939
Watercolour and pencil
15 ¼ x 10 ¾ inches
Provenance: The Estate of Randolph Schwabe

Randolph Schwabe lived at 20 Church Row, Hampstead
from 1929-1945.

118 (below, right)
Dover Seafront
Signed with initials, inscribed 'Dover' and dated 1935
Watercolour
14 ¾ x 10 ½ inches
Provenance: The Estate of Randolph Schwabe

119

Tackley's Inn, Oxford
Signed, inscribed 'Oxford' and dated 1943
Watercolour with pencil
9 ¾ x 12 ¼ inches
Provenance: The Estate of Randolph Schwabe
Exhibited: The Art Exhibitions Bureau, London;
New English Art Club, London

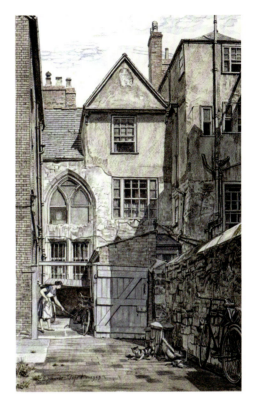

120

Windmill Hill, Hampstead
Signed, inscribed with title and
dated 1939
Watercolour and pencil
10 ¾ x 13 ¼ inches
Provenance: The Estate of
Randolph Schwabe

121
Sheep Dipping
Inscribed 'Lanteglos' and dated 1932
Charcoal with watercolour on tinted paper
15 ¼ x 17 ¾ inches
Provenance: The Estate of Randolph Schwabe
Literature: Gill Clarke, *Randolph Schwabe*,
Bristol: Sansom & Company, 2012
Preliminary drawing for 'Sheep Dipping' 1932,
Tyne and Wear Archives and Museums.

An image of the finished picture appears in
Gill Clarke, *Randolph Schwabe*, Bristol:
Sansom & Company, 2012, page 70.

Latneglos-by-Fowey is beside the tidal estuary of
the River Fowey on the south Cornwall coast.

122
Ducks in the River, Kilve, Somerset
Inscribed 'Kilve' and dated 1933
Watercolour and ink
14 ¾ x 18 ¼ inches
Provenance: The Estate of Randolph Schwabe

123

East Cliff Dover
Signed, inscribed with title and dated 1947
Watercolour with pencil
11 ½ x 12 ¾ inches
Provenance: The Estate of Randolph Schwabe

Schwabe's painting shows the houses on East Cliff and Athol Terrace, Dover. Instead of an uninterrupted view of the sea, these houses now overlook the entrance to the Dover Ferry Terminal.

124
Seated Female Nude
Ink
7 ¼ x 5 ¾ inches
Provenance: The Estate of Randolph Schwabe

125
Playing the Piano
Dated 1931
Ink and watercolour
14 x 10 inches
Provenance: The Estate of Randolph Schwabe

126
**Reclining Nude
on a Pillow**
Pencil
8 ¼ x 12 ½ inches
Provenance: The Estate of
Randolph Schwabe

127
**Standing Nude
with Linked Hands**
Dated 1943
Pastel
14 ¼ x 6 ¾ inches
Provenance: The Estate
of Randolph Schwabe

129
Relaxed nude
Pastel
14 x 6 ¾ inches
Provenance: The Estate of Randolph Schwabe

128
Seated Nude, Looking Down
Pastel
10 ¾ x 16 ¼ inches
Provenance: The Estate of Randolph Schwabe

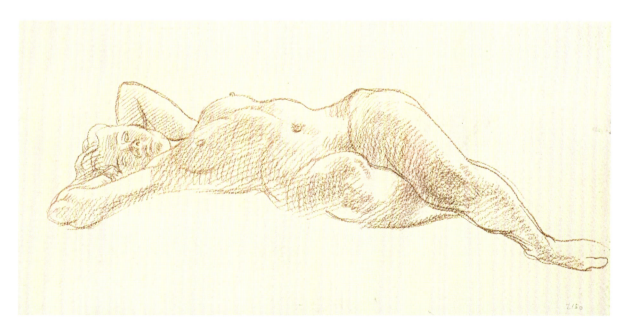

JOB NIXON

Job Nixon, RWS RE NEAC (1891-1938)

Though a painter as well as a printmaker, Job Nixon was best known as an etcher of landscapes and figure subjects. He was the first to win the scholarship for engraving at the British School at Rome, and during his time in Italy he produced *An Italian Festa*, **the large and complex plate that made his name. On his return to London, he soon became assistant to Malcolm Osborne in the engraving school of the Royal College of Art. During the later years of his short career, he worked in Cornwall and taught at the Slade School of Fine Art.**

For a biography of Job Nixon, please refer to page 147.

130
Demolition of Devonshire House, Piccadilly
Signed and inscribed with title
Etching
9 ½ x 14 ½ inches

Devonshire House was demolished in 1924.

CHARLES TUNNICLIFFE

Charles Frederick Tunnicliffe, OBE RA RE VPSWLA (1901-1979)

One of the foremost wildlife artists of the twentieth century, Charles Tunnicliffe displayed his talents in an impressive range of formats and media, including watercolours, oils, etchings and wood engravings.

For a biography of Charles Tunnicliffe, please refer to *Chris Beetles Summer Show*, 2017, pages 119-120.

131
Eagle Owls
Signed
Watercolour
28 x 15 ¾ inches

CHARLES KNIGHT

Charles Knight, VPRWS ROI (1901-1990)

The Sussex landscape painter, Charles Knight, channelled the tradition of English watercolour painting in order to produce his own original contribution. As a result, he became a pillar of the

132
Devon River
Signed
Signed, inscribed with title, artist's address and 'No 1' on labels on reverse of canvas and frame
Oil on canvas
27 ¼ x 35 ¼ inches
Provenance: Garnet R Wolseley
Literature: Michael Brockway, *Charles Knight RWS, ROI*, Leigh-on-Sea: F Lewis, 1952, page 109, (catalogue no 273, study illustrated plate 38)
Exhibited: Royal Academy, 1947, no 501

Probably the River Lyn, which flows from its source in Exmoor, Somerset through the East Lyn valley in Devon.

Royal Society of Painters in Water-Colours and received acclaim, from William Russell Flint, as the 'star turn' of the Recording Britain scheme.

For a biography of Charles Knight, please refer to *Chris Beetles Summer Show*, 2008, page 24.

134 (opposite, below)
Summer Day
Signed
Oil on canvas
29 ½ x 39 ¾ inches
Literature: Michael Brockway, *Charles Knight, RWS, POI*, Leigh-on-Sea: F Lewis, page 101 catalogue no 198
Exhibited: Royal Academy, 1944;
Brighton Art Gallery, 1944;
Royal Society of British Artists, 1947 (by invitation)

133

Elberry Cove, South Devon
Signed
Watercolour
10 ½ x 14 ¼ inches

The small pebble beach of Elberry Cove is close to Paignton and still only accessible by foot.

The building at the end of the beach is Lord Churston's bath house. Once consisting of three storeys and a thatched roof, it had a ground floor that would flood when the tide came in. Lord Churston and his guests could then swim straight out to sea through a gated doorway. The building also had an early version of a hot tub, with a fire heating up the seawater to warm bathers after their swim.

Close to Agatha Christie's home, Greenway, Elberry Cove was not only one of her favourite bathing spots. but features in one of her novels, *The ABC Murders*, as the setting of Sir Carmichael Clarke's untimely death.

ROWLAND HILDER

Rowland Frederick Hilder, OBE PRI RSMA
(1905-1993)

A highly fluent watercolourist, Rowland Hilder became synonymous with the Kent countryside that he painted for much of his life. He was a wide-ranging painter and illustrator, who tackled cityscapes, marines and figure subjects with equal confidence and success.

For a biography of Rowland Hilder, please refer to
Chris Beetles Summer Show, 1998, page 20.

135
Pulteney Bridge, Bath
Watercolour and ink
10 x 13 ¾ inches
Exhibited: 'Recording Britain: the Twentieth Century Landscape',
Chris Beetles Gallery, London, February 2008, no 69

136
Landscape with Sheep
Signed
Watercolour with ink
19 ½ x 16 ½ inches
Provenance: Leslie Hill and by descent
Illustrated: *John Bull*, 1 July 1950, cover

The *John Bull* magazine, was published by Odhams Press. They commissioned some of Britain's finest illustrators and featured covers that encapsulated post-war Britain.

STANLEY ROY BADMIN

Stanley Roy Badmin, RWS RE AIA FSIA (1906-1989)

Throughout his career, S R Badmin used his great talents – as etcher, illustrator and watercolourist – to promote a vision of the English countryside and thus of England itself. By underpinning his idealism with almost documentary precision and detail, he was able to produce images that appealed to all, and could be used for a great variety of purposes, from education through to advertising. The wellbeing suggested by each rural panorama is all the more potent, and pleasing, for the accuracy of **each tree and leaf, and the plausibility of the slightest anecdotal episode.**

For a biography of Stanley Roy Badmin, please refer to *Chris Beetles Summer Show*, 2017, page 124.

His etchings are represented in numerous public collections, including the British Museum; the Ashmolean Museum (Oxford); Aberystwyth University School of Art; and the Herbert F Johnson Museum of Art, Cornell University (NY).

137
Lower Standen. Nr Folkestone Kent
Signed
Signed with initials, inscribed with title and dated 1926-7 below mount
Pencil sketch of a pig's head below mount
Watercolour with ink
6 ½ x 9 ¼ inches
Exhibited: Probably the work exhibited at 'Watercolours and Etchings by S R Badmin, ARWS, ARE', Fine Art Society, London, June 1937, no 5

138 (opposite)
Henley Royal Regatta
Signed
Inscribed 'Henley Royal Regatta viewed from the bridge.
The artist (in the bottom left corner) looks at the detailed scene with some trepidation' below mount
Watercolour with bodycolour and ink
12 ¾ x 10 ¼ inches
Provenance: Leslie Hill and by descent
Illustrated: Designed for but not illustrated in *John Bull* magazine, c1955, cover

The *John Bull* magazine, was published by Odhams Press. They commissioned some of Britain's finest illustrators and featured covers that encapsulated post-war Britain.

S.R.Badmin

139
A British Common
[Clapham Common]
Signed with initials, inscribed
'London Common' and dated 1939
Ink and watercolour
6 x 9 ¼ inches

Preliminary drawing for the
Artists International Association
Everyman print produced as a zinc
lithoplate in 1939.

140
Clapham Common
Signed, inscribed with title and dated 1936
Watercolour
6 x 10 inches
Exhibited: 'Watercolours and Etchings by S R Badmin, ARWS, ARE',
Fine Art Society, London, June 1937, no 38 as 'Clapham Common – Autumn'

BETTY SWANWICK

Ada Elizabeth Edith Swanwick, RA RWS (1915-1989)

Very early in her career, Betty Swanwick established herself as an illustrator and designer of great wit and invention, so complementing her friend and teacher, Edward Bawden. Later, she produced an extraordinary series of visionary watercolours and drawings in the tradition of William Blake and Samuel Palmer, which led to her election as a full member of the Royal Academy.

For a biography of Betty Swanwick, please refer to *Chris Beetles Summer Show*, 2019, pages 104-105.

Her work is represented in the collections of the Royal College of Art and Blackburn Museum and Art Gallery.

141
The Right Chair for the Occasion
Signed and dated '82
Pencil and watercolour
22 x 18 ½ inches
Literature: Paddy Rossmore, *Betty Swanwick: Artist and Visionary*, London: Chris Beetles Gallery, 2008, pages 102 and 109
Exhibited: Royal Academy Summer Exhibition, 1983, no 127;
'Betty Swanwick R.A. A Narrative Process', Royal Academy, London, 2001, no 36

BERNARD DUNSTAN

Andrew Harold Bernard Dunstan,
RA PRWA NEAC HPS (1920-2017)

Bernard Dunstan was brought up in the tradition of Degas, Sickert and Vuillard, and established himself with intimate figure subjects and landscapes in paint and pastel. A member of both the Royal Academy and the New English Art Club for many years, he was much loved and greatly respected.

For a biography of Bernard Dunstan, please refer to *Chris Beetles Summer Show*, 2019, page 106.

His work is represented in The Royal Collection, the Royal West of England Academy and numerous public collections, including the National Portrait Gallery.

142
The Studio
Signed with initials
Inscribed with title and dated '3-4 98' on reverse
Oil on canvas
15 x 20 inches

143
The Family Tea
Signed with initials
Inscribed with title
and dated 1953
on reverse
Oil on board
7 ¾ x 11 ½ inches

144
San Gimignano
Signed with initials
Signed, inscribed with
title, and dated '71'
on reverse
Oil on board
9 ½ x 12 inches
Exhibited: New Grafton
Gallery, London, June 1972

145
Interior, Morning (Triptych)
Signed with initials on each canvas
Inscribed with titles and dated 'Diana Standing (In Nightdress)
92-94', 'Interior, Mirepoix 94' and 'Diana Standing (Nude)
92-94' on reverse of each canvas
Oil on three canvases
Left panel: 41 ½ x 17 ½ inches
Centre panel: 41 ½ x 35 ¼ inches
Right panel: 41 ½ x 17 ½ inches

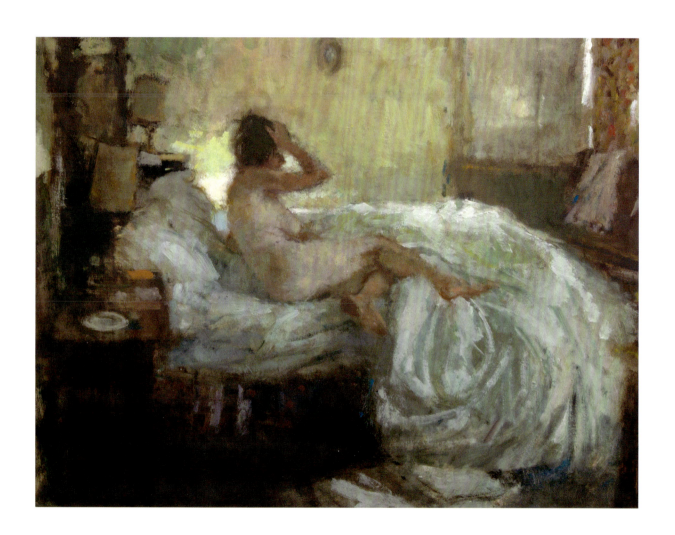

146

Morning, Lisbon
Signed with initials
Inscribed with title and '15', and dated 4.91 on reverse
Signed, and inscribed with title, medium and artist's
address on Royal Academy label on reverse
Oil on board
14 ¾ x 17 ¼ inches

147

In the Cabin
Signed with initials
Signed and inscribed with title, medium and artist's address on Royal
Academy label on original backboard
Pastel on tinted paper
13 x 13 ¼ inches
Exhibited: Royal Academy Summer Exhibition, 1994, no 754

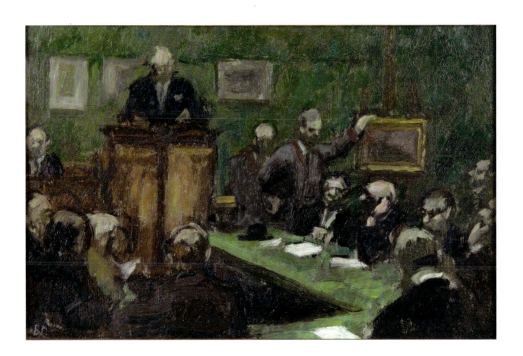

Auction at Sotheby's
Signed with initials
Signed, inscribed with title
and 'Peter Wilson Auctioneer',
and dated 'Painted 1960'
on reverse
Oil on board
7 ½ x 11 ½ inches
Provenance: Thomas Agnew
& Sons, London

149
**Council Meeting,
Royal Academy,
Sir Charles Wheeler,
Sir Basil Spence,
Sir Henry Rushbury**
Oil on board
8 ½ x 9 ¼ inches
Exhibited: Roland, Browse
and Delbanco, London

It was between 1962-1964
that Sir Charles Wheeler as
President, served on the
Council of the Royal Academy
with both Sir Basil Spence as
Treasurer and Sir Henry
Rushbury as Keeper.

150 (above)
Three Sketches
First sketch inscribed 'I'm keeping this one!'
and '9" x 12" (on canvas)';
Second sketch inscribed 'in the show'
and '11" x 11 ½"';
Third sketch inscribed 'in the show' and '11" x 10"'
Pencil
11 ½ x 7 ¾ inches

151 (above, right)
Standing Nude, Interior
Signed with initials twice
Pastel on tinted paper
11 ¾ x 10 ½ inches

152 (right)
Interior, Llwynhir
Signed with initials
Pastel
13 ¾ x 12 ¾ inches

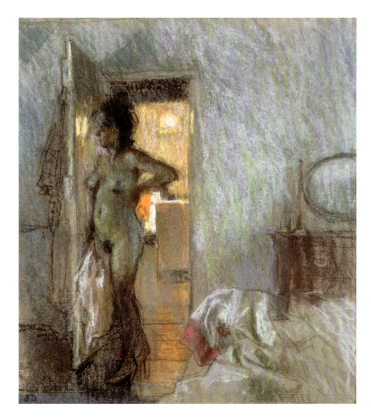

RAYMOND BOOTH

Raymond Charles Booth (1929-2015)

Intensely private, and possessing an obsessive work ethic and passion for the natural world, Raymond Booth earned a reputation as one of the greatest botanical painters and illustrators, despite rarely leaving his Yorkshire home. Eschewing the more fashionable modernist principles of the early mid-twentieth century, he instead produced beautiful, intense compositions in oil of British flora and fauna, that rival the very finest Victorian followers of the genre.

For a biography of Raymond Booth, please refer to
Chris Beetles Summer Show, 2018, page 138.

153
Badger and Honeysuckle
Signed
Oil on board
16 x 15 inches

154
**Autumn, a Fox
Resting Amongst
the Fallen Leaves**
Signed
Oil on board
25 x 19 ½ inches

VAL ARCHER

Val Archer (born 1946)

Blurring distinctions between still life, interior and the record of architectural detail, Val Archer has developed a highly original and absorbing body of work. Attentive to the aesthetic pleasures of life, she handles paint sensitively and sensuously, and keeps alive the canvas and paper through thrilling combinations of colour, texture and motif. Flowers, fruits and fabrics are set against complex, resonant surfaces to encapsulate feelings for places and cultures.

For a biography of Val Archer, please refer to page 148.

155 (above)
Tea for Two
Signed with initials
Oil on paper
13 ½ x 16 ½ inches

156 (left)
Cherry Stones
Signed with initials
Oil on paper
29 x 21 inches

157 (opposite)
A Ripe Summer Basket
Signed with initials
Oil on paper
26 x 19 inches

LESLEY FOTHERBY

Lesley Fotherby (born 1946)

Multi-talented and multi-faceted, Lesley Fotherby goes from strength to strength in expanding her range and increasing her popularity. She perpetually strives to capture the moving world around her, with fresh approaches and new appeal.

For a biography of Lesley Fotherby, please refer to page 149.

158
Horses and Teasel
Signed
Inscribed with title on reverse
Oil on canvas
24 x 30 inches

159 (right)
Berries in the Snow
Signed
Oil on canvas
24 x 30 inches

160 (below, left)
Tree,
The Bay of Aphrodite
Signed
Inscribed with title
on reverse
Oil on canvas
22 x 16 inches

161 (below, right)
Bank of Dandelion
Clocks, Devon
Signed
Inscribed with title
on reverse
Oil on canvas
30 x 23 ½ inches

GERALDINE GIRVAN

Geraldine Girvan (born 1947)

Geraldine Girvan has been exhibiting at the Chris Beetles Gallery for over 35 years and, in that time, she has consistently proven that the strong tradition of Scottish colourists is still very much alive.

For a biography of Geraldine Girvan, please refer to page 150.

162 (left)
Tortoise Shell Cat and Poppies
Signed
Signed, inscribed with title and 'Edinburgh', and dated 2008 on reverse
Oil on linen
28 x 26 inches

163 (below)
Studio Still Life
Signed and dated '00
Signed, inscribed with title and 'Edin', and dated 'Dec 2000' on reverse
Oil on linen
46 x 50 inches

164 (left)
Red Studio
Signed
Signed, inscribed with
title and 'Edin' and
dated '06 on the
stretcher
Oil on linen
26 x 25 inches

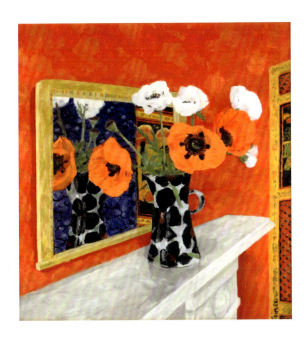 

165 (right)
Bright Day
Signed and dated '05
Inscribed with title and
dated 05 on reverse
Bodycolour on paper
22 ½ x 30 ½ inches

166
White Cloth
Signed and dated '93
Signed, inscribed with title
and dated '93 on reverse
Watercolour
29 ½ x 32 ¾ inches

MELISSA SCOTT-MILLER

Melissa Scott-Miller, RBA RP NEAC (born 1959)

Melissa Scott-Miller is an acclaimed painter of meticulously detailed urban landscapes and portraits of people in their surroundings.

For a biography of Melissa Scott-Miller, please refer to page 150.

167 (left)
Wisteria Doorway in Islington, Spring 2024
Signed with initials and dated 24
Signed and inscribed with title on reverse
Oil on linen
20 x 16 inches

168 (right)

The April Gardener
Signed with initials and dated 24
Oil on canvas
39 ¼ x 31 inches

'Suddenly everything was bursting out in wonderful fresh greens and yellows and lots of purple blooms. In this painting, I have put my neighbour cutting down the ivy that has got a bit too overgrown. My neighbours are incredible gardeners, I'm very grateful for the lovely view they provide.'

Melissa Scott-Miller, May 2024

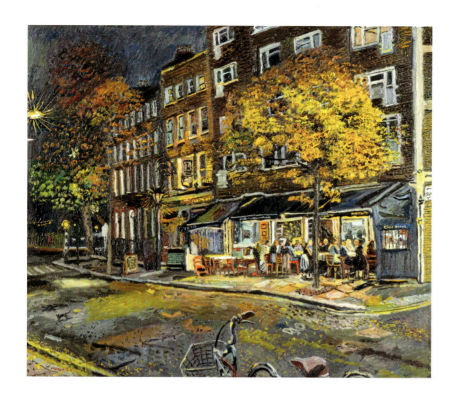

**Ciao Bella restaurant,
Lambs Conduit Street
on an Autumn night 2023**
Signed with initials and dated 23
Signed and inscribed with title on reverse
Oil on canvas
20 ¼ x 24 inches

170
Blossom in Mayfair
Signed with initials and dated 24
Signed on reverse
Oil on canvas
23 ½ x 23 ½ inches

"There is a subtlety and a frisson in these paintings that transcends both the application of the paint and the image on the canvas. It is a sense of time, the sense of a moment held.

Like the disquiet of déjà vu, what we are shown affects us on two levels. Initially it is a finely observed and executed view – a tree, a door, a railway cutting – images that are familiar and comfortable but appear simultaneously to be imbued with a drama or a foreboding that is barely implied. Perhaps the drama is occurring just outside the frame or maybe we are being shown the stage after or before the performance.

This ability to imply great emotional force above and beyond the temporal image within a figurative narrative genre is a rare talent of real genius."

A A Gill (art critic, journalist and author)

171
February at the Regents Canal
Back of Noel Road and Vincent Terrace 2024
Signed with initials and dated 24
Signed and inscribed with title on reverse
Oil on canvas
20 x 30 inches

ENZO PLAZZOTTA

Enzo Plazzotta (1921-1981)

For a biography of Enzo Plazzotta, please refer to page 151.

The Italian-born sculptor, Enzo Plazzotta, gained a major international reputation. Though he retained close links to his native country, it was in London that he established his sculptural practice in the 1960s, and was first celebrated. Throughout his career, he exhibited widely in Europe, the United States and Australia. He produced inventive and engaging compositions in marble and bronze, especially of human and animal figures in movement. He developed a particular rapport with dancers, and worked with some of the most celebrated performers of his day. His output encompasses both personal expressions of his sensibility and highly accessible, popular works, many of which grace our public spaces.

Published in 1986, this first edition catalogue Raisonné contains a biographical introduction to Plazzotta by his daughter Carol, as well as an introduction by critic Max Wykes-Joyce.

The catalogue Raisonné illustrates all Plazzotta's cast work in bronze from the aesthetically graceful statuettes to the bolder, more personal statements. It also lists his major portrait commissions and documents the special editions of his work in acrylic, silver and gold.

Copies are available from Chris Beetles Gallery.

A major retrospective exhibition of the work of Enzo Plazzotta will be held at Chris Beetles Gallery in Spring 2025.

172

Downfall, 1967
Stamped with the Plazzotta seal and inscribed 6/12
Bronze with a rich brown patina
22 ½ x 19 x 12 inches
Literature: Carol Plazzotta and Richard O'Conor, *Enzo Plazzotta. A Catalogue Raisonné*, London: Trefoil Books, 1986, page 30, Catalogue Raisonné no 49
Exhibited: Stowe School, 1969; Acquavella, New York, 1969; Italian Institute, London, 1976

173

The Three Graces, 1977
Stamped with the Plazzotta seal and inscribed 7/9
Stamped with the foundry stamp Meridian Bronze
Bronze with rich brown patina
39 ½ x 29 ½ x 29 ½ inches
Literature: Carol Plazzotta and Richard O'Conor,
Enzo Plazzotta. A Catalogue Raisonné, London:
Trefoil Books, 1986, pages 146-7,
Catalogue Raisonné no 271

Exhibited: Wildenstein, London, 1978;
Wildenstein, New York, 1980;
Bedford College, London, 1980;
Freeland, London, 1985

The Three Graces, from Greek mythology, represent the
daughters of Zeus, each of whom were able to bestow a
particular gift to humanity – Euphrosyne (mirth), Aglaea
(elegance) and Thalia (youth and beauty).

SYDNEY HARPLEY

Sydney Harpley, RA FRBS (1927-1992)

The work of Sydney Harpley always surprised and delighted: dancers, acrobats, girls on swings were posed and executed with equal audacity and elegance. Establishing the single female as his favourite subject while still a student, he rose to become the most popular sculptor, not only among Royal Academicians but among all who exhibited at the Royal Academy Summer Exhibitions.

For a biography of Sydney Harpley, please refer to *Chris Beetles Summer Show*, 2015, page 67.

Chris Beetles Gallery represents the Estate of Sydney Harpley.

174
Nude Study 1991
Signed (back of chair) and numbered 12/12 (side of chair)
Bronze
4 ¾ x 4 ¾ x 2 inches
Literature: *Royal Academy Illustrated*, 1991, page 82
Exhibited: Royal Academy Summer Exhibition, 1991, no 998

Number twelve from an edition of twelve

On a slate base measuring 5 ½ x 2 x ½ inches

175
Dancer Adjusting Her Shoe 1989
Signed and numbered 0/9 (left flounce of skirt)
Bronze
21 x 15 x 17 inches
Provenance: The Estate of Sydney Harpley
Exhibited: Royal Academy Summer Exhibition 1989, no 840;
'Sydney Harpley RA. New Sculptures', Chris Beetles Gallery, London, 1990, no 8
Artist's proof from an edition of nine
On a travertine base measuring
11 ¼ x 8 ¼ x 1 ¼ inches

176

Girl in a Deckchair 1990
Signed and numbered 6/9
(on back of chair)
Bronze
11 x 18 x 6 ½ inches
Exhibited: Duncalfe Fine Art,
Harrogate, November 1988,
no 25;
'Sydney Harpley RA, New
Sculptures', Chris Beetles Gallery,
London, 1990, no 7

Number six from an edition
of nine

177

Girl in a Deckchair 1991
Signed and numbered 8/9
(on back of deckchair)
Bronze
9 ½ x 17 x 6 ¾ inches
Exhibited: Royal Academy
Summer Exhibition, 1991, no 637

Number eight from an edition
of nine

JAMES BUTLER

James Walter Butler, MBE RA FRBS RWA (1931-2022)

One of Britain's foremost figurative sculptors, James Butler was well known for both his public commissions, large and small, and his personal compositions. Having gained a thorough grounding in carving early in his career, he then developed equal mastery as a modeller. He created many cherished monuments in Britain and abroad that stand securely in a tradition that can be traced from Donatello to Charles Sargeant Jagger to Giacomo Manzù.

For a biography of James Butler, please refer to pages 152-153.

178
Girl on a Bicycle
Signed, numbered V/X and dated 2019
(on bronze base by back wheel)
Bronze
16 ¾ x 14 x 6 inches
Exhibited: Royal Academy Summer Exhibition, London, 2019, no 780;
'The Figurative Tradition, A Celebration of Contemporary British Art', Chris Beetles Gallery, London, October-November 2020, no 39;
Royal Academy Summer Exhibition Memorial Display, London, 2022, no 799

Number five from an edition of ten

On a Kilkenny stone base measuring 15 x 4 ½ x 3 ½ inches

179
The Golden Tutu
Signed with initials, numbered 10/10 and dated '16 (on bronze base)
Bronze
12 x 6 ¾ x 4 ¾ inches
Literature: John Meulkens, *James Butler an Extended Personal View of a Collector*, Radway: John Meulkens and James Butler, 2013 (Third Edition), page 20 (Illustrated)
Exhibited: Royal Academy Summer Exhibition, 2018, no 785

Number ten from an edition of ten

Green Howards Memorial, Crépon

A maquette for an over life-size sculpture commissioned for the Green Howards memorial at Crépon in Normandy, 1996.

'The Regiment was one of only two in the British Army to land two assault battalions on D Day, when CSM San Hollis stormed across an orchard in Crépon in his second action to win the only VC that day. In recognition of this, in October 1996, a bronze statue of a Green Howard was unveiled in Crépon by King Harald of Norway, to commemorate those Green Howards who gave their lives in Normandy and in the Second World War. The imposing statue by James Butler is deeply moving in portraying an exhausted but resolute infantryman resting on a broken wall and reflecting on that day's historic events.'

(Geoffrey Powell & John Powell, *The History of the Green Howards*, Barnsley: Leo Cooper, 2002, page 259)

180

Cellist 2009

Signed and numbered III/X
Bronze
18 ½ x 13 x 13 ¼ inches
Literature: John Meulkens, *James Butler an Extended Personal View of a Collector*, Radway: John Meulkens and James Butler, 2009 (Second Edition), page 91 (Illustrated)
Exhibited: Royal Academy Summer Exhibition, London, 2020, no 1136;
'James Butler RA Remembered', Chris Beetles Gallery, London, May-June 2023, no 33
Number three from an edition of ten

On a Kilkenny stone base measuring 14 ½ x 12 x 1 ¾ inches

181

Green Howards Memorial, Crépon

Signed, inscribed with title and dated '96 (on stones at rear)
Bronze
18 ½ x 11 x 13 inches
Exhibited: Royal Academy Summer Exhibition, London, 1996, no 1172, as 'Sketch Model of Soldier for the Green Howards Memorial at Crépon, Normandy';
'James Butler RA Remembered', Chris Beetles Gallery, London, May-June 2023, no 24
From an edition of twelve
On a black slate base measuring 11 ¼ x 10 ½ x ¾ inches

Biographies

FRANCIS WHEATLEY

Francis Wheatley, RA (1747-1801)

Francis Wheatley is best known as a painter of landscapes, portraits and figures in a sentimental and pretty style. His most popular and notable works were the *Cries of London*, a series of fourteen paintings of London street scenes which were then engraved and published in pairs.

Wheatley was born in London in 1747 and was the son of a Master Tailor. He was introduced to the study of drawing via his neighbour, Daniel Fournier, a drawing-master and artist. His father then moved him to William Shipley's Academy in London, a prodigious drawing school which later became Ackermann's Repository of Arts. During his time studying at Shipley's, Francis Wheatley was awarded several prizes by the Society of Arts, including a prize for figurative drawing for students under the age of sixteen.

Francis Wheatley first exhibited with the Society of Artists in 1765 with *Portrait of a Gentleman*, and later became a member in 1770 and then director in 1774. He enrolled at the Royal Academy Schools in 1769 and swiftly built a reputation as a skilled painter. He established a friendship with the artist John Hamilton Mortimer who greatly influenced his work; it has been suggested by Francis Wheatley's obituarist in the *Gentleman's Magazine* that through his friendship with Mortimer his work 'acquired a style more pure'.

In 1778 Wheatley exhibited for the first time at the Royal Academy, amongst the five paintings displayed were *A wood scene, with gypsies telling a fortune* and *View near Ivy Bridge, Devonshire.*

Despite his artistic abilities and growing reputation, Wheatley fell into significant debt. In 1779 he seduced the wife of the artist Alexander Gresse and fled with her to Ireland to escape his creditors. Whilst in Dublin he painted *The Irish House of Commons,* which was received very well, as well as several portraits of political figures. In 1783 he was forced to return to London when his seduction and elopement with Mrs Gresse became known, he had been pretending she was his wife whilst in Ireland. Wheatley married artist Clara Maria Leigh in 1786 and they had four daughters.

Once back in London, having fallen into debt again, he approached the publisher and print seller John Boydell for work. Whilst working under Boydell's patronage Wheatley created the work that he is perhaps best known for, the *Cries of London*, made up of fourteen paintings designed for engraving. They depict predominantly pretty female merchants and street vendors, in a sentimental in style.

Wheatley exhibited regularly at the Royal Academy throughout his life, he was elected an associate of the Royal Academy in 1790 and then Royal Academician in 1791. He continued to be plagued with debt for the rest of his life,. Additionally he suffered ill health. His chronic gout during the 1790's meant he was unable to work for long periods at a time, his 'youthful irregularity and temperance' was cited as the cause. He taught his wife, Clara Maria Leigh, to paint and draw so that she could support herself and their four children during his periods of debilitating illness. Francis Wheatley died in 1801 aged 54.

JOHN CONSTABLE

John Constable RA (1776-1837)

One of the most significant and important British artists of the 19th century, John Constable is best known for his paintings of the English countryside, particularly those representing his native Stour Valley, Suffolk, an area that came to be known as 'Constable Country'. His highly original approach to landscape painting and his lifelong dedication to the genre resulted in a remarkable body of work that has ensured that his contribution to the development of British landscape art is rivalled only by that of his contemporary, J M W Turner.

John Constable was born 11 June 1776 in East Bergholt, Suffolk, the fourth of six children of Golding Constable, a wealthy miller and merchant, and his wife Ann (neé Watts). His father owned a substantial house and grounds with views of the Stour Valley in all directions, and this environment would form a prominent feature of his art throughout his life. Though he developed an interest in painting from an early age, Constable reluctantly began training to join his father's business at the age of sixteen. However, in 1795, he met the distinguished painter and patron Sir George Beaumont, who encouraged him to pursue a career as an artist. The following year, he was introduced to two professional artists, John Cranch and J T Smith, who provided the young Constable with practical instruction and further strengthened his desire to become a painter. Nevertheless, it was only in 1799, when his younger brother Abram turned sixteen and took his place as the heir to the family business, that John Constable felt freed from his obligations to his family.

In February 1799, with the grudging approval of his father, John Constable left for London and the following month entered the Royal Academy Schools. At this time, art academies stressed history painting as the most appropriate subject matter for their students and Constable was initially restricted to the antique academy, until he was enrolled as a student in the life academy in February 1800. Though now based in London, John Constable made frequent trips back to his native Suffolk countryside to paint and draw, indulging his enduring passion for the English landscape. Certainly by 1802, the year he refused a post as drawing master at a military academy, Constable's letters indicate his commitment to the study of nature that would be the foundation of his art. That year, he exhibited at the Royal Academy for the first time and over the next few years made sketching tours to the Peak District, the Kentish coast and the Lake District. Though under pressure from his parents to become financially independent, he remained a student of the life academy until 1808 and also resorted to painting portraits, finding subjects through family and friends.

By 1809, though Constable was regularly exhibiting at the Royal Academy and British Institution, he was still struggling financially and his income was still being supported by his parents. His resolve to succeed as an artist was intensified that year when he began a courtship with Maria Bicknell, whom Constable is likely to have first met a number of years earlier when she was a twelve year old child visiting her grandfather, Durand Rhudde, the rector of East Bergholt. Over the next five years, Constable divided his time between London and Suffolk, continuing to paint portraits to earn a living whilst also striving to earn a reputation and fame as a landscape painter. Throughout this period, Maria Bicknell's family vigorously resisted their relationship. Though the deaths of Constable's mother in 1815 and his father the following year were emotionally traumatic for him, they did provide him with an inheritance and the easing of a financial burden that provided him with the means to marry Maria Bicknell, which he did in October 1816.

In December 1817, the first of Constable's seven children, his son John, was born and, motivated by the need to support his family, he strove for further success and recognition. He began to paint on a large scale, with the Stour scene, *The White Horse*, exhibited at the Royal Academy in 1819, garnering public attention and critical approval and helping to bring about his election as an Associate of the Royal Academy. This success initiated a series of well-received paintings, including *Stratford Mill* (1819-1820), *View on the Stour near Dedham* (1822) and *The Lock* (1824). One of his best-known works, *The Hay Wain* (1821), earned Constable international success when it was shown in 1824 at the Paris Salon, where it won a gold medal that was awarded by the French king, Charles X. In 1828, his work *The Vale of Dedham*, secured him election to become a Royal Academician. However that same year Maria, who had exhibited symptoms of tuberculosis since 1819, sadly died, marking the start of a decline in Constable's mental and physical health from which he did not recover.

From 1829, John Constable remained active in his duties with the Royal Academy. That year he exhibited *Hadleigh Castle* at the Academy and worked with the engraver David Lucas on a series of mezzotints after his works that were published as a suite of prints entitled *English Landscape*. In 1836, he submitted his final Royal Academy entry, *Cenotaph to the Memory of Sir Joshua Reynolds, Erected in the Grounds of Coleorton Hall, Leicestershire, by the Late Sir George Beaumont*. His health had been worsening over a number of years and on 31 March 1837 he fell ill on his way home from a charitable event and passed away in the early hours of the following morning, at the age of sixty.

SAMUEL PROUT

Samuel Prout, OWS AA (1783-1853)

Despite persistent ill health, Samuel Prout developed as a highly distinctive topographical artist and undertook regular sketching tours, first in Britain and later on the Continent. The resulting images of ancient buildings at their most picturesque were highly popular and influential – as exhibition watercolours and, especially, lithographic illustrations.

Samuel Prout was born at Trevil Street, Plymouth, Devon, on 17 September 1783, the fourth of fourteen children of a shopkeeper and naval outfitter. As a child, he suffered from severe sunstroke, which gave him violent headaches for the remainder of his life. They were so debilitating that he had to take to his bed once or twice a week until his marriage in 1810. He was also victim to chronic lung congestion.

Prout made sketches and copied prints as a young child, and received encouragement from his headmaster, the Rev John Bidlake, when he attended Plymouth Grammar School. He was also given some lessons from Thomas H Williams. The Plymouth area became well known to him through the many sketching expeditions he undertook with his friend and fellow pupil, Benjamin Robert Haydon, who became a history painter.

Haydon's father was a printer, publisher and bookseller, who kept a shop in the Market Place in Plymouth. There, in 1801, Prout met the budding antiquary, John Britton, who was in town to look for materials for the projected topographical survey, *Beauties of England and Wales*. (This collaboration with E W Brayley was published in parts between 1803 and 1815).

Prout joined Britton on a tour of Cornwall, in order to make drawings for *Beauties*, but he had problems with the perspective of the buildings, and had to work hard through the following year in order to improve his skills.

Aware of the artist's potential, Britton persuaded Prout to move to London in 1802, and live with him at his home, 21 Wilderness Row, Clerkenwell. There he entered a circle of topographical illustrators that included Frederick Mackenzie and George Sidney Shepherd. He was set to copy the work of leading contemporary watercolourists, including William Alexander, J M W Turner, John Sell Cotman, Thomas Girtin and Thomas Hearne, the last three having a particular influence on his early style. He was also sent on sketching tours of Cambridgeshire, Essex and Wiltshire during the years 1803 and 1804, as preparation for work on *Beauties and The Architectural Antiquities of Great Britain* (5 vols, 1806-26). During the same period, he began to exhibit at the Royal Academy of Arts and make useful contacts with dealers,

including Thomas Palser of Surrey Side, Westminster Bridge, who was the earliest purchaser of his work.

In 1805, Prout became so ill that he had to return to Plymouth, though he was well enough to make a sketching tour of Devon and Cornwall in the October of that year. During his prolonged stay at home, he gave Charles Lock Eastlake his first drawing lessons.

By 1808, Prout had returned to London, and was living at 55 Poland Street, Soho. He brought with him many West Country coastal scenes, which he exhibited at the Royal Academy, the British Institution and the Associated Artists in Water Colours (becoming a member of the last in 1810, and remaining so until its demise in 1812). These scenes would also provide the basis for *Picturesque Delineations in the Counties of Devon and Cornwall*, published by Palser in 1812.

Establishing himself as a drawing master, Prout taught at Dr William Glennie's academy in Dulwich Grove, from 1809 to 1821, during which time his pupils included (the Rev) J D Glennie and William Henry Harriott, two future amateur artists. He also attracted a private clientele of about thirty, one of his first pupils being James Duffield Harding (who followed Prout to become a landscape painter and lithographer).

Marrying in Brixton in 1810, Prout and his wife, Elizabeth Gillespie moved into 4 Brixton Place (now part of Brixton Road) in the following year. Once settled, he began to capitalise on his teaching, by producing a series of drawing books for the use of the beginners, starting with *Rudiments of Landscape in Progressive Studies* (1813, containing 16 aquatints). Over three decades, Prout issued fourteen publications, which, while falling into either drawing manuals or volumes of topographical plates, together promoted the taste for the Picturesque.

Not neglecting his career as an exhibiting artist, Prout began to show work at the Society of Painters in Oil and Water-Colours in 1815, becoming an associate in 1817 and a member in 1819. (The society returned to its former name of the Society of Painters in Water Colours in 1821.)

Prout's style and subject matter were profoundly affected by his first Continental sketching tour, to Northern France in 1819. Keen to meet the challenge of recording the ancient architecture in all its atmospheric detail, he found inspiration in the recent drawings of Norman buildings by Henry Edridge. The death of Edridge in 1821 left the way free for Prout to exploit the genre, and his regular travels (until 1846) provided him with constant material.

Through the 1820s, Prout took in France, the Low Countries, Germany (including the Rhineland and Bavaria), and Italy (of which Venice proved an inevitable highlight). Sometimes, he travelled and sketched in the company of other artists, as with Richard Parkes Bonington in St Omer (1822).

In order to reproduce his graphic responses accurately and vividly, Prout turned from aquatint to lithography, as is seen to great effect in *Picturesque Buildings in Normandy* (1821, printed by Charles Hullmandel) and *Illustrations of the Rhine* (1822-26). The most notable later volumes included *Facsimiles of Sketches made in Flanders and Germany* (1833) and *Facsimiles of Sketches made in France, Switzerland and Italy* (1839). The breadth of his travels, and the resulting range of images, ensured Prout a strong reputation on both sides of the Channel, a reputation that reached its height around 1830. His contacts in the Parisian art world included Baron Isidore Taylor, who helped him to show watercolours at the Paris Salon of 1824, and who, in the following year, included lithographs of his work in the third volume of *Voyages pittoresques et romantiques dans l'ancienne France* (produced by Taylor in collaboration with Charles Nodier).

Back in England, Prout received a number of honours and mixed freely with fellow leading artists. In 1829, George IV appointed him 'Painter in Water-Colours in Ordinary to His Majesty', an honour renewed by both William IV and Queen Victoria; while, a year later, he became a fellow of the Society of Antiquaries. During the early 1830s, he regularly attended the Artists' and Amateurs' Conversazione, where he met with Thomas Shotter Boys, John Sell Cotman, David Cox, David Roberts and Clarkson Stanfield.

However, in 1836, ill health drove Prout from London to Hastings, where he spent eight years in what he regarded as exile. On his return to the capital, in 1845, he settled at 5 De Crespigny Terrace, where he became a neighbour of the young critic, John Ruskin, who was a great admirer of his work. Making his last Continental tour, to Normandy, in 1846, he then produced gradually less work until his death at home on 10 February 1852. His studio sale was held at Sotheby's on 19-22 May 1852.

Prout's distinctive style, and Ruskin's promotion of it, continued to prove highly influential. What may be termed the Prout effect was sustained into the late nineteenth century by Samuel Gillespie Prout and John Skinner Prout (respectively his son and nephew), and also through aspects of the work of T R C Dibdin and Louis Haghe. In 1879, the Fine Art Society published *Notes by Ruskin on Samuel Prout and William Hunt: illustrated by a Loan Collection of Drawings*.

His work is represented in numerous public collections, including the British Museum, The Courtauld Gallery, Tate and the V&A; The Fitzwilliam Museum (Cambridge), Manchester Art Gallery, Plymouth City Museum and Art Gallery, Royal Cornwall Museum (Truro), Southampton Art Gallery and The Whitworth Art Gallery (Manchester).

JAMES THOMAS WATTS

James Thomas Watts RBSA, RCamA (1853-1930)

As a follower of John Ruskin and the paintings of the Pre-Raphaelites, James Thomas Watts dedicated himself to painting the truth of nature, particularly through woodland landscapes. Best known for this narrow range of subject matter, he meticulously explored these scenes through the different seasons and times of day, in order to develop subtleties of light that produced astonishingly atmospheric works.

James Thomas Watts was born in Birmingham and educated in the city at King Edward's School and the Birmingham School of Art. As he became familiar with the writings of John Ruskin and the paintings of the Pre-Raphaelites, he held fast to the principle of truth to nature, and applied it in particular to woodland landscapes. While working within what was a narrow range of subject matter, he explored its every aspect through the seasons and at different times of day, and represented the most subtle effects of light with astonishing atmosphere and detail. After his move to Liverpool, in about 1874, he painted mainly in North Wales and North-West England, though also visited the North-East, Scotland and even the Low Countries. He exhibited the resulting watercolours, and some oils, at leading institutions; these included the Royal Academy, the Royal Institute of Painters in Water-Colours and the Royal Society of British Artists, and – as a member – the Royal Birmingham Society of Artists, the Birmingham Art Circle, the Liverpool Academy and the Royal Cambrian Academy. In 1883, he married Louisa Margaret Hughes, also a landscape painter. He died in Liverpool on 24 October 1930.

Chris Beetles Gallery rekindled interest in the work of J T Watts from the 1980s and over twenty years curated a significant group of eighteen watercolours for the prominent watercolour collector David Fuller. Further interest was generated by the auction of the Fuller Collection of Victorian Landscape Watercolours at Christies's London in April 2000, when record prices were achieved and significant lots were acquired by the Metropolitan Museum of Art, New York.

ETHEL ATCHERLEY

Ethel Atcherley (1864-1905)

Known primarily as a landscape artist, depicting rustic scenes in watercolour and oil, Ethel Atcherley was also a talented sculptor, exhibiting work in this medium in her native Manchester. Before her premature death at the age of 41, she saw her works displayed at the Royal Academy of Arts, Manchester Academy of Fine Arts and the Royal Society of British Artists.

Ethel Atcherley, was born in Eccles, Lancashire on 30 January 1864. She was fourth child and second daughter of Roger and Mary Ann Atcherley. From an early age she was brilliantly creative, focusing on her passion for music and painting. As a teenager, in 1880, Ethel Atcherley was awarded Second Class Honours in her Local Examinations in Elementary Musical Knowledge. However, she decided to further her education in art studies and enrolled at Manchester School of Art. She was there from at least 1885 as records show she won the school's Sketching Club Prize on 13 January 1886. Although now known for her landscape work, Ethel Atcherley studied modelling alongside painting and in 1891 Manchester Art Gallery's First Exhibition of Arts and Crafts displayed her sculpture *Reduced Copy of 'The Slave' by Michelangelo*. For the following few years of the early 1890s, Ethel Atcherley continued her training at Lambeth School of Art, and then in Paris. She specialised in watercolours and oils and most often depicted rustic scenes taking influence from the geography surrounding her. On her return to England in 1895, her work became increasingly recognized and the local press took interest. That same year, Ethel Atcherley's paintings, including *Anglesea Village*, began to be exhibited at the Royal Academy. Meanwhile she was elected an associate of Manchester Academy of Fine Arts in 1896 and in 1900 Ethel Atcherley was advanced to member. Whilst The Royal Academy of Arts progressively exhibited her paintings, other major galleries including the Royal Society of British Artists and the Walker Art Gallery, Liverpool showed her work too. Ethel Atcherley died age 41 in 1905. Most of her work remains in family ownership.

ALBERTO PISA

Alberto Pisa (1864-1936)

Alberto Pisa was an Italian watercolourist and landscape artist best known as a painter of architectural and genre scenes of Italian towns. His association with the Macchiaioli movement influenced his commitment throughout his career to capturing beauty in nature and urban scenes through subtleties of light and shade.

Alberto Pisa was born on 19 March 1864 in Ferrara, in the Emilia-Romagna region of Italy. As a young man, he studied in his hometown under Gaetano Domenichini (1786-1864) before moving to Florence to study at the Academy of Fine Arts. Whilst in Florence, he became part of what was known as the Macchiaioli movement, a group of Florentine and Tuscan artists who moved away from the rigid, rule-bound practices of the Italian academicians and instead looked to nature for instruction in order to capture natural light, shade and colour.

Alberto Pisa spent the early years of his career exhibiting across Italy to growing critical and commercial success. Two of the first pictures he exhibited, *Chiesa de Santa Maria Novella* and *Donne e Madonne*, in Venice in 1887, received much critical praise. In 1888, he exhibited two paintings in Bologna, *Fra e Polli* and *Tempo Ladro*. The latter was purchased by the Ministry of Education to be displayed at the National Gallery of Rome. The following year, he exhibited a further two artworks in Florence. Later in his career, he returned to Ferrara and began to take portrait commissions from the lords and ladies of the town.

In 1901, a review in *The Times* of an Italian exhibition featuring Pisa's work referred to his watercolours of Italian towns as 'charming; both in the details of architecture and in general town views he is far beyond the average of the men who paint picturesque Italy'. It is possible that this review brought Pisa to the attention of the publishers, A & C Black, and in 1904 they commissioned him to produce a series of paintings of Rome. The collection was published as *Rome. Painted by Alberto Pisa* and the artworks, along with some of Umbria, were exhibited at the Fine Art Society in London in 1905. A review of the exhibition in *The Times* described how, 'Mr Pisa shows us Rome full of lights and air, and aglow with beautiful colours in stone and trees and flowers'. The publication on Rome was followed by *Pompeii. Painted by Alberto Pisa* (1910) and *Sicily. Painted by Alberto Pisa* (1911). Many of his illustrations were also reproduced in subsequent mixed volumes by A & C Black, as well as in newspapers.

In the latter years of his career, Alberto Pisa continued to paint architectural and genre scenes, largely in the Tuscan region. He died in Florence on 15 July 1930. His work is represented in the collections of the National Gallery of Modern Art, Rome, the Palazzo dei Diamanti, Ferrara, and the Bristol City Museum.

CARLO PELLEGRINI

Carlo Giovanni Battista Pellegrini (1866-1937)

The Italian-born Carlo Pellegrini was known as a talented painter in oil and tempera of snowy landscape scenes in his native northern Italy. A move to the Swiss Alps saw Pellegrini develop into a popular illustrator of postcards and posters extolling the excitement of winter sports such as skiing and ice skating. His reputation as an admired painter of sporting scenes led him to participate in the 1912 Olympic Games in Stockholm, where he became the first man to win an Olympic Gold Medal for Painting.

Carlo Giovanni Battista Pellegrini was born on 25 October 1866 in Albese (known today as Albese con Cassano) in the Como region of Lombardy, Italy. As a young man he indulged in his interest in art by drawing from life, before moving to Milan to study painting at the Accademia di Belle Arti di Brera. As a young man, Pellegrini exhibited regularly in solo and group exhibitions across Northern Italy, including at the Brera Biennale, where he became an honorary member in 1897.

In 1900, Pellegrini moved to Switzerland, first to Geneva, where he worked as an artistic advisor in the publishing house Vouga & Co, and then to the village of Adelboden in the Swiss Alps. Here, he established a reputation as a skilled painter of snowy landscape scenes, particularly featuring sporting activities such as skiing and skating. Many of these sporting scenes were reproduced as postcards and posters designed to promote tourism.

Perhaps the most significant event of his career occurred in 1912, when Baron Pierre de Coubertin, President of the International Olympic Committee, invited Pellegrini to participate in the arts competition at the 1912 Stockholm Olympic Games. These were the first Games to hold art competitions, with medals awarded in five categories: architecture, literature, music, painting and sculpture. Carlo Pellegrini won the gold medal for painting, becoming the first man to win an Olympic medal for painting. Artistic competitions remained a part of the Olympic Games until 1948, but were discontinued due to concerns about amateurism and professionalism. The work for which he won the gold medal, entitled *Winter Games*, was a large triptych comprised of three wall friezes. The whereabouts of the original artwork is unknown and it was possibly destroyed in a major fire at the Vouga & Co. publishing house in Geneva, where chromolithographs had been produced.

In 1917, Carlo Pellegrini returned to his hometown of Albese, where he continued to paint the surrounding landscapes. He died there on 5 September 1937.

EDWARD HANDLEY-READ

Edward Harry Handley-Read, MBE RBA (1870-1935)

Establishing himself as a wide-ranging artist and illustrator during the 1890s, Edward Handley-Read produced pioneering images of the front line during the First World War.

Edward Handley-Read was born Edward Read in London. He was possibly the son of Henry Read, and his wife, Emma (née Birch), who, in 1881, were keeping an upmarket lodging house at 65 Sloane Street. He was educated at Kensington Grammar School and first studied art at the National Art Training School (more popularly known as the South Kensington Schools). He then progressed to Westminster School of Art, where he worked under Frederick Brown, and the Royal Academy Schools, where he won the Creswick Prize for landscape painting. He exhibited at the Royal Academy of Arts, the Royal Institute of Painters in Water Colours and the Royal Society of British Artists, becoming a member of the last in 1895. He also contributed illustrations to various books and magazines, including *The Graphic* and *The Illustrated London News*. During the 1890s, he gave as his addresses the Ranger's Lodge, Hyde Park (1890-94), and 1 Camden Studios, Camden Street (1893-98). By 1911, he was working at 8 Camden Studios.

In 1902, Edward Read married Sarah Elizabeth Clarke in Edmonton. However, she died a few years later and, in 1911, he married Eva Handley in Kingston upon Thames. She was a pioneering woman dental surgeon and suffragette, and in deference to her he changed his surname by deed poll to Handley-Read. They would have a son and a daughter.

During the First World War, Edward Handley-Read served in the Machine Gun Corps, first as a Sergeant-Instructor and later a Captain. In that capacity, he organised an army studio for diagrams and models for instruction on military matters, instructed on camouflage, and invented published sets of coloured diagrams for the teaching of machine-guns. He also produced several hundred watercolours of life on the front line, some of which were exhibited at the Leicester Galleries in a series of solo shows entitled 'The British Firing-Line', the first of which took place in May 1916. In the following year, the gallery published a portfolio of his colour engravings under the same title, which had a foreword by Hilaire Belloc.

By 1916, the Handley-Reads had established a home in Steyning, Sussex, where other members of Eva's family were living. It was there in that year that their son, Charles, was born. He would become a noted architectural writer and collector, (with an innovative interest in William Burges), and an inspiring teacher, at Bryanston.

After the war, Edward Handley-Read produced a variety of figure subjects and landscapes. Living at Chantry Lodge, Chantry Lane, Storrington, Sussex, until at least 1932, he died at the House of Steps, 41 High Street, Salisbury, on 6 December 1935.

His work is represented in the collections of the Imperial War Museums.

CECIL ARTHUR HUNT

Cecil Arthur Hunt, VPRWS RBA (1873-1965)

Once elected a full member of the Royal Society of Painters in Water-Colours in 1925, Cecil Arthur Hunt retired from his career as a barrister and turned his serious pastime of painting into a profession. While he had first established himself as a painter of mountains, especially the Alps and the Dolomites, he soon proved himself a master of a great variety of topographies. The impressive, often stark, effects that he achieved rival those associated with his friend and mentor, Frank Brangwyn.

Cecil Arthur Hunt was born in Torquay, Devon, on 8 March 1873, the second of three children of the highly regarded writer and geologist, Arthur Roope Hunt, and his wife, Sarah (née Gumbleton), who was born in Waterford, Ireland. He was educated at Winchester and Trinity College, Cambridge, studying Classics and Law, and being called to the Bar in 1899 (as had his father before him). He treated painting and writing as serious pastimes until 1925, when he was elected to the full membership of the Royal Society of Painters in Water-Colours. He then relinquished his legal career to become a professional painter.

Hunt had first exhibited in London in 1900, at the Alpine Club Galleries, and had held his first major show a year later, alongside E Home Bruce at the Ryder Gallery. From the first, he established himself as an atmospheric painter of mountains, especially of the Alps and Dolomites. However, he was soon accepted as a master of a great variety of topographies, for he exhibited the products of his wide travels frequently and extensively. Favourite destinations included the West Country, the West Coast of Scotland, the Rhône Valley, Northern Italy, Rome and Taormina, Sicily.

In 1903, Hunt married Phyllis Lucas, and they would have two sons. From 1911, they lived at Mallord House, on the corner of Mallord Street and Old Church Street, Chelsea, which was especially designed for them by Ralph Knott to include a large studio on the ground floor. During the summer months, he and his family retreated to the farm estate of Foxworthy, on the edge of Dartmoor, in Devon.

During the First World War, Hunt was employed at the Home Office, first in connection with Irish prisoners interned in England following the Sinn Fein's Rebellion in 1916, and later assisting the Committee for Employment of Conscientious Objectors.

Hunt showed work regularly at the Royal Academy of Arts (from 1912), the Royal Society of British Artists (from 1914) and the Royal Society of Painters in Water-Colours (from 1918). He was elected a member of the Royal Society of British Artists in 1914, an associate of the RWS in 1919, and a full member six years later. He acted as the Vice-President of the RWS for a three-year period from 1930. His many substantial solo shows included six at the Fine Art Society (1919-34) and one at Colnaghi's (1945). Following his death on 5 August 1965, he was the subject of a large memorial show at the Royal Society of Painters in Water-Colours.

Chris Beetles Gallery has done much to revive interest in the work of Cecil Arthur Hunt. A large scale retrospective exhibition was held in Ryder Street in 1996 at his London gallery, on the exact site of the artist's first substantial show in 1901. The retrospective was accompanied by a definitive catalogue.

His work is represented in the collection of the Royal Watercolour Society and numerous public collections, including the V&A.

FREDERICK LANDSEER MAUR GRIGGS

Frederick Landseer Maur Griggs, RA RE (1876-1938)

Frederick Landseer Maur Griggs was considered to be one of the finest and most respected etchers of his generation. Influenced as a young man by the work of Samuel Palmer, he created stunning and dramatic compositions of gothic buildings and haunting landscapes, guided by his religious upbringing and training as an architectural draughtsman.

Frederick Landseer Griggs was born on 30 October 1876 in Hitchen, Hertfordshire, the eldest of four children of Frederick Griggs and his wife, Jemima (neé Bailey). His parents were Baptists and he grew up in religious surroundings. His father, though a baker and confectioner by trade, was a deacon of the local church and his mother gave Bible classes. The family attended a newly built chapel and its Neo-Gothic architecture would have a lasting effect on his artistic vision across his career. As a child, he attended school locally in Hitchen, before moving to London to study at the Slade School of Fine Art and train as an architectural draughtsman under the architect Walter Millard. In 1895, he moved to the offices of Charles Edward Mallows, working there until 1897, when he returned to Hitchin to set up his own studio. The same year he exhibited an architectural drawing for the first time at the Royal Academy.

In 1900, Frederick Landseer Griggs was commissioned by the publishers Macmillan & Co to produce drawings for the Hertfordshire book in their major series, *Highways and Byways*. This would become the most substantial achievement of his career. Over the remaining 37 years of his life, he would illustrate twelve volumes of the series. He was still working on the project at his death, leaving some drawings unfinished. In 1903, he moved to Chipping Campden in the Cotswolds, where the previous year, the Guild and School of Handicraft had been established by the architect and designer, Charles Robert Ashbee. Griggs became closely associated with the Guild, taking lodgings in the guild hostel in 1904 before moving to Dover's House in the High street, where he would live until 1930.

Religion remained a significant part of Frederick Landseer Griggs's life, and in 1912 he was received into the Catholic Church, adopting the baptismal name 'Maur'. To mark the occasion he designed a bell, named 'Maurus', for the local church of St Catherine's. The following year he produced the striking plate *Maur's Farm*, with five variant states produced between 1913 and 1922. During this period of his life in Chipping Campden, he also established himself as a successful illustrator, developing a style that moved beyond architectural topography into more imaginative compositions that evoked the history and spirit of the places he recorded. In 1916, he was elected an associate member of the Royal Society of Painter-Etchers and Engravers. In 1918 he became a fellow, and was elected to the council two years later.

Frederick Landseer Maur Griggs continued to work as an architect, primarily on small-scale projects in and around Chipping Campden. A lasting contribution to his craft was made in 1919, when he designed a series of war memorials. These memorials, located at Broadway, Snowshill, Painswick, Upton St Leonards and Chipping Campden, were completed pro bono and still stand today.

In the postwar period, Frederick Landseer Maur Griggs's designs became ever more ambitious and dramatic. From 1922, he established his own press to prove his plates. This allowed him to revise some of his past works, such as adding rich meteorological effects to the skies of his earlier plates. That year, he became one of the few etcher associates of the Royal Academy. On 9 January 1922, he married his studio assistant, Nina Blanche Muir at Brompton Oratory. Together they would have a son, John Coelfrid, and five daughters, Mary, Millicent, Hilda, Barbara and Agnes. In 1931, he was elected a Royal Academician and served on the Academy selection committee in 1933. In 1934, he was elected Master of the Art Workers' Guild.

Frederick Landseer Maur Griggs struggled with his health throughout much of his adult life. The financial strains of his large family, coupled with the economic difficulties that followed the Wall Street Crash of 1929 contributed to his frailty. He died at his home on 7 June 1938 at the age of 61 and was buried at St Catherine's Church in Chipping Campden.

JOB NIXON

Job Nixon, RWS RE NEAC (1891-1938)

Though a painter as well as a printmaker, Job Nixon was best known as an etcher of landscapes and figure subjects. He was the first to win the scholarship for engraving at the British School at Rome, and during his time in Italy he produced *An Italian Festa*, **the large and complex plate that made his name. On his return to London, he soon became assistant to Malcolm Osborne in the engraving school of the Royal College of Art. During the later years of his short career, he worked in Cornwall and taught at the Slade School of Fine Art.**

Job Nixon was born at 16 Charles Street, Stoke-on-Trent, Staffordshire, on 20 February 1891, the fourth of five children of the pottery printer, Job Nixon, and his wife, the pottery painter, Mary (née Ellerton). He grew up among pottery decorators and, on leaving school, entered the engraving department of Mintons. He was subsequently apprenticed to an engraver who supplied copper plates for transfer printing to local pottery manufacturers. In the evenings, he studied at Stoke School of Art. However, he soon changed direction, becoming a butcher's assistant, and rapidly succeeding in the trade, so that, while he was still in his teens, he employed four assistants, who helped him run two shops and a stall in Stoke Market Hall. He did not neglect his studies in art, and produced his own advertising, while also taking a position as assistant master at Burslem School of Art. By his late teens, he was living with his family at 240 London Road, Stoke-on-Trent.

In 1910, Nixon won a scholarship to the Royal College of Art, in London, and there studied etching under Sir Frank Short. In 1915, while still a student, he began to exhibit at the Royal Academy of Arts. However, following the outbreak of the First World War, he joined the 4th Eastern Company of the Army Service Corps, during which time he produced theatrical scenery for camp entertainments. On his release in 1918, he took advantage of an army scholarship to further his studies under Henry Tonks at the Slade School of Fine Art. Ever enterprising, he also painted decorations for shop windows and bazaars and worked with the theatrical designer, Hugo Rumbold, at Covent Garden Opera.

In 1920, Nixon won the first scholarship of engraving to be endowed by the British School at Rome. As a result, he spent three years in Italy (and France), and produced, among other works, the large plate, *An Italian Festa*, which brought him to the attention of the public and, in 1923, led to his election as an associate of the Royal Society of

Painter-Etchers and Engravers. He was also appointed to a teaching post in the Engraving School of the Royal College of Art, as an assistant to Malcolm Obsborne, who succeeded Frank Short on his retirement in 1924. At this time, he was living at 45 Redcliffe Road, Chelsea.

In 1925, Nixon married Helen Wigan in Kensington, and they settled at Pembroke Walk Studios, later moving to Oakfield Street. However, by June 1929, he had begun an affair with Nina Berry, who was then an artist student, and this led to his wife divorcing him in 1930 on the grounds of adultery. During this period, he joined the New English Art Club, and joined and resigned from the Art Workers' Guild.

Nixon was visiting Cornwall from at least as early as 1929, when he exhibited two watercolours of Falmouth. In 1931, at the urging of his friend, Lamorna Birch, he and Nina Berry settled in the county, at Riverside Studios, Lamorna Cove, so becoming members of Birch's colony of artists. In that year, his painting, Gypsies, made a great impression as his first exhibit with the Newlyn Society of Artists, and won the 'position of honour'. He was elected a member of the Royal Society of Painter-Etchers and Engravers in 1933, and of the Royal Society of Painters in Water-Colours in 1934.

In 1934, Nixon and Berry moved to St Ives. They worked at St Peter's Studio and also ran a school of painting in Back Road West. However, a year later, they returned to London, and settled at 36 Danvers Street, Chelsea, so that Nixon could take up a teaching post at the Slade School of Fine Art. He also taught at Gravesend School of Art around this time.

Nixon married Nina Berry in Chelsea, in 1937, but died the following year, on 26 July 1938, while they were holidaying in their horse-drawn caravan at Mendham, Norfolk. A memorial group of his works was included later that year in the fifth annual exhibition of the Society of Staffordshire Artists, while a memorial exhibition of his paintings was held at the Colnaghi Gallery, London, in March 1939.

His work is represented in numerous public collections, including the British Museum and the V&A; the Ashmolean Museum (Oxford) and The Potteries Museum & Art Gallery (Stoke-on-Trent); and the Fine Art Museums of San Francisco (CA).

VAL ARCHER

Val Archer (born 1946)

Blurring distinctions between still life, interior and the record of architectural detail, Val Archer has developed a highly original and absorbing body of work. Attentive to the aesthetic pleasures of life, she handles paint sensitively and sensuously, and keeps alive the canvas and paper through thrilling combinations of colour, texture and motif. Flowers, fruits and fabrics are set against complex, resonant surfaces to encapsulate feelings for places and cultures.

Val Archer was born in Northampton and was educated there at the High School for Girls. While still at school, she attended on Saturday mornings Henry Bird's drawing classes at Northampton School of Art. A painter of the old school, Bird was helpful and encouraging: as useful and illuminating as his rigorous approach to life-drawing was his knowledgeable passion for the Italian masters. Already a compulsive worker, Archer would typically spend the rest of her weekend painting, either outside or back at home, sharing the kitchen table while her mother cooked.

In 1964 Archer left Northampton to study at Manchester College of Art and Design. For her at this time this was the ideal environment and she still speaks warmly of the stimulation and instruction she received. A wide-ranging pre-diploma year, during which she particularly enjoyed the sculpture, was followed by a three-year painting course. Norman Adams was head of painting, teaching by example rather than instruction, and the majority of the staff were young and energetic artists at the beginning of their careers. Art history was taught; a liberal studies course introduced unfamiliar music and ideas; and for the first time, Archer encountered contemporary art from the USA, finding herself most drawn to the Pop artists and those moving away from abstract expressionism – Jim Dine, Jasper Johns and Robert Rauschenberg. A very different but equally profound enthusiasm formed at this time was for Pierre Bonnard: the Royal Academy's exhibition devoted to him in 1966 made a lasting impression.

Val Archer graduated from Manchester in 1968 and, feeling she 'needed more time', moved to London to study painting at the Royal College of Art. Here she found a very different atmosphere: some of the teachers maintained a distant attitude to the students and not all of them encouraged an interest in contemporary American art. Despite this, she made several trips to the USA in the late Sixties and early Seventies, principally to New York. An offer of representation by a New York gallery raised the possibility of making a career there, but she decided to return to the UK. Back in London, themes and subjects began to appear which would feature in her work for many years. The most important of these was a fascination with painting textiles – in particular, the landscape-like forms they assume when draped or folded. She graduated from the RCA in 1971, winning the Anstruther Prize for painting.

Life after college began with a flat in a mansion block in Brixton, which had space for a studio, and a job with a printer in Streatham. An opportunity to show her work soon arose: the gallery-owner Basil Jacobs had seen her paintings at the RCA and displayed some in his Bruton Street gallery in 1972-73. Her first solo show came soon after, in Stuttgart in 1975. This was a success, and her time in Germany was made memorable also by her discovery of Otto Dix and a visit to Colmar to see Grünewald's Isenheim altarpiece. There were further solo shows in Europe: at Robert Noortman in Maastricht, in 1989 and 1990. In the UK she exhibited with Fischer Fine Art from 1979 to 1981, and from 1993 to 1997 with Christie's Contemporary Art in London and elsewhere. Her work was represented in the Royal Academy Summer Exhibition in 1993, 1995 and 2003. In 1998 she had her first solo exhibition at the Chris Beetles Gallery and has shown there regularly ever since.

For most of the 1970s and 1980s Val Archer combined painting with teaching. She is characteristically modest about this. 'It used to worry me', she says. 'I used to worry I wasn't good enough'. Nevertheless, she enjoyed a long association with Sheffield College of Art, which led to her Stuttgart exhibition, and has taught at Wolverhampton and Lanchester Polytechnics and Winchester, Cheltenham, Cardiff and Goldsmiths' College Schools of Art.

Since 1990 Val Archer's name has become known to a wider public through her work in newspapers, magazines and books. For three years her paintings accompanied food and cookery articles in the *Sunday Telegraph* and the *BBC Good Food* magazine. Two books on fruit appeared in 1993 and 1994, and she also illustrated one of Nigel Slater's early cookery books. Her most recent publication is *The Painter, the Cook and the Art of Cucina* (2007), a collaboration with the Italian cookery writer Anna del Conte which explores the culinary traditions of six regions of Italy.

Travel has long been a pleasure and a source of inspiration for her: in recent years she has tended to stay close to the Mediterranean. After a visit to the painter Joe Tilson in Tuscany in 1999 she bought a house and studio nearby and she now paints both there and at her home in Clapham. Her studios are spacious and beautiful, the workspace of someone who values order and efficiency. Apart from the tools of her trade they contain little – minimal furniture, some books, a small collection of objects which may become subjects. She likes to have music playing as she paints and begrudges time spent away from her work. Looking back at her childhood she says, 'I always painted', and she probably always will.

LESLEY FOTHERBY

Lesley Fotherby (born 1946)

Multi-talented and multi-faceted, Lesley Fotherby goes from strength to strength in expanding her range and increasing her popularity. She perpetually strives to capture the moving world around her, with fresh approaches and new appeal.

Lesley Fotherby was born Lesley Dixon in Kingsbury, North London, on 24 June 1946, the daughter of an engineering draughtsman for Westrex and a hairdresser. She was educated at Roe Green Infant School (1951-57) and Copthall County Grammar School for Girls, Mill Hill (1957-64). Following a foundation course at Bath Academy of Art, at Corsham (1964-65), she studied fashion and textiles at Ravensbourne College of Art and Design, in Bromley, where she numbered Zandra Rhodes among her teachers (1965-68). Teacher training at Leicester Polytechnic (1968-69) prepared her to teach art at Hatters Lane County Secondary School for Girls in High Wycombe, Buckinghamshire (1969-71). While in High Wycombe, she met her future husband, fellow teacher, David Fotherby.

Following a move to Yorkshire in 1971, Lesley continued to teach, most notably at a school in Richmond. However, from 1977, she gave more time to painting, and in that year attended a course at West Dean College on botanical illustration. This proved a turning point in her work, particularly in her use of watercolour. Her botanical illustrations became regular contenders in the shows of the Royal Horticultural Society, achieving one silver and two silver-gilt medals in the early 1980s.

While exhibiting at the Chandler Gallery, Leyburn, in 1983, Lesley met Chris Beetles, who encouraged her to paint full time. And so, though she began intermittent adult art teaching with an evening class at a school in Wensleydale, she gave up school teaching. Lesley's increased focus and productivity led, in 1985, to 'Nature Through the Seasons', the first of many solo shows at the Chris Beetles Gallery, and one that helped establish her as a sensitive painter of subtle, atmospheric landscapes. In addition, she has also become a regular contributor to the gallery's annual Summer Shows and Cat Shows.

In 1992, Lesley started painting dancers at the Northern School of Contemporary Dance in Leeds, then at several other dance schools, including the Central School of Dance, Northern Ballet and London City Ballet. Her interest in form and movement developed from this early figurative work, and continues to combine motion and spontaneity with an adeptness and fluidity of representation both in oil and watercolour – from the simple flurry of a line and the bleed of a wash, to her closely observed and richly perceived and perfected portrayals.

Also in 1992, Lesley wrote and illustrated *The Cat Who Came to Stay*, an early stage on her way to becoming one of the country's most admired painters of cats. Subsequent publications have included *Cats: Drawing and Painting in Watercolour* (1993) and six books by Doreen Tovey, for which she provided the illustrations: *Cats in May* (1993), *Cats in the Belfry* (1993), *Double Trouble* (1994), *The New Boy* (1994), *More Cats in the Belfry* (1995) and *The Coming of Saskia* (1995).

Since her move to Little Eversden, in Cambridgeshire, in 2001, Lesley has been Artist-in-Residence with both the City of Cambridge Symphony Orchestra and the Lucy Cavendish Singers, while also continuing to paint dancers, particularly those of Birmingham Royal Ballet.

Having long been established as a painter of landscapes, Lesley Fotherby began, in 2005, to capture the drama and beauty of the sea, again in both oil and watercolour. Together with her images of the countryside, dancers and cats, her seascapes reveal a continuing pleasure and passion for the movement and rhythms of the world around her.

Since 2006, Fotherby has held seven exhibitions with the Chris Beetles Gallery: 'The Traditional and Spontaneous Eye' (2006), 'The World in Motion' (2011), 'Sunlight and Spotlight' (2014) and 'Walking with Nature, Dancing for Joy' (2016), 'Lesley Fotherby' (2019), 'Lesley Fotherby's Winter' (2021) and 'New Oils of the Seasons and Ballet Pieces' (2022).

GERALDINE GIRVAN

Geraldine Girvan (born 1947)

Geraldine Girvan has been exhibiting at the Chris Beetles Gallery for over thirty five years and, in that time, she has consistently proven that the strong tradition of Scottish colourists is still very much alive.

Born in Derby in 1947, Geraldine studied at Edinburgh University and trained at Edinburgh College of Art. She was influenced by both the college's Principal, Sir William Gillies, and her tutors, Elizabeth Blackadder and Alex Campbell, who contributed in providing a decisive inspiration in the direction of her career. Of Campbell she has written that he:

Opened my eyes to the qualities of touch and paint handling and [that his] own work was often idiosyncratic in composition and painted with great subtlety.

Like many Scottish painters before her, Girvan has drawn energy from the vital tradition of the French colourists, notably Bonnard and Matisse. The resulting work, in oil and watercolour, tends to present a domestic paradise, by blurring the distinction between interior and exterior, and also between objects and surfaces. Floral prints suggest a landscape beyond; tangled borders mimic wallpaper. Mirrors ensure light and space, while seeming to propagate fruit and flowers; screens and blinds create tantalizing views, and her reclining cats accentuate this atmosphere of languorous comfort.

In addition to regular shows at Chris Beetles Gallery, she has exhibited at the Royal Scottish Academy, the Royal Scottish Society of Painters in Watercolour and the Royal Watercolour Society.

MELISSA SCOTT-MILLER

Melissa Scott-Miller, RBA RP NEAC (born 1959)

Melissa Scott-Miller is an acclaimed painter of meticulously detailed urban landscapes and portraits of people in their surroundings.

Melissa Scott-Miller grew up in Kensington, London, and studied at the Slade School of Fine Art. She was taught by Anthony Green, Lucian Freud, and Jeffrey Camp; who said of her work:

'A child prodigy is rare in music or mathematics but very rare in painting. For Melissa, the picture comes whole, erasure and overpainting seem unnecessary. The visible world is easily grasped. The multiple components are handled with the assurance of a virtuoso.'

She won numerous accolades from the Slade, twice including prizes judged by Carel Weight, whom she admires greatly to this day.

Since graduating in 1981 with a first class degree, Melissa Scott-Miller has shown work at numerous galleries and with such leading exhibiting societies as the Royal Academy, the Royal Society of British Artists, the Royal Society of Portrait Painters, and the New English Art Club. Her urban landscapes focus on the London streets she frequents, with the ability to keenly observe detail as both artist and local.

Her portraits have been exhibited five times at the National Gallery as part of the annual Portrait Awards. She has held solo shows across the UK at the Albemarle Gallery, Grosvenor Gallery, Mark Jason Gallery, and the Twenty Twenty Gallery in Ludlow. She has also held solo exhibitions in America at the Acquavella in New York, and the Cross Gate Gallery in Lexington, Kentucky.

The numerous awards that she has received include the Lynn Painter-Stainers Prize in 2008. She is a member of the Royal Society of British Artists, the Royal Society of Portrait Painters and the New English Art Club.

Melissa teaches at Heatherley's School of Fine Art, London, and the Royal Drawing School. In March 2023, Chris Beetles Gallery held her first solo, sell-out exhibition, and they have continued to show regular displays of her work ever since. In 2023 her painting *The Greeting* was exhibited in the Royal Academy Summer Exhibition, and already this year she has exhibited at the Mall Galleries twice, for the annual NEAC and RPP shows.

Melissa is also regularly working on commissions, and can be spotted painting around the city.

ENZO PLAZZOTTA

Enzo Plazzotta (1921-1981)

The Italian-born sculptor, Enzo Plazzotta, gained a major international reputation. Though he retained close links to his native country, it was in London that he established his sculptural practice in the 1960s, and was first celebrated. Then, throughout his career, he exhibited widely in Europe, the United States and Australia. He produced inventive and engaging compositions in marble and bronze, especially of human and animal figures in movement. He developed a particular rapport with dancers, and worked with some of the most celebrated performers of his day. His output encompasses both personal expressions of his sensibility and highly accessible, popular works, many of which grace our public spaces.

Enzo Plazzotta was born in Mestre, near Venice on 29 May 1921, and grew up on the shores of Lake Maggiore. Developing a particular aptitude for sculpture, he began to study under Messina at the Accademia di Brera, in Milan, at the age of seventeen. However, he had to terminate his studies abruptly when Italy entered the Second World War. A volunteer in the Bersaglieri, he was sent to North Africa, where he was awarded the Silver Medal for valour. Following the fall of Mussolini in 1943, he broke with the Fascist regiment and helped to found a partisan group in the Italian mountains. Betrayed by an infiltrator, he was captured and placed in solitary confinement, escaping six months later while in transit to Mauthausen. In Switzerland, he helped to improve relations between the partisans and the Allies. In the closing months of the war, he returned to Italy to participate in the final struggle for national liberation.

Plazzotta was finally able to return to the Brera to complete his studies, under Manzù, who exerted a considerable influence over his work. On graduating, he received a commission from the Italian Committee of Liberation to make a bronze statuette for presentation to the British Special Forces Club. He travelled to London himself to present the statuette and was so drawn to the British way of life that he decided to stay.

Plazzotta found work as a portrait artist but, later, with a family to support, he was obliged to turn to more lucrative pursuits. Rather than practise his art merely as a hobby, he set up a commercial art agency in London, which specialised in importing Milanese art and design. It was not until the early 1960s that he found himself in a position to take up sculpting again. Engaging himself fully in his work, he produced both accessible pieces and more personal projects in which he overcame conceptual and technical problems.

Favourite preoccupations included dancing figures, horses and adaptations of classical and Christian themes. Retaining close links with his native Italy, he kept a small studio in Pietrasanta, near Carrara; it was the base for much casting of his work, and for experiments in carving marble and onyx. In 1976 he received the title of Cavaliere from the Italian government for services to art. In the same year he moved into the Garden Studio in Cathcart Road, built and formerly owned by Sir Charles Wheeler. He contracted cancer in 1981 and died in the same year.

His work is represented in numerous public collections, including the Stanley Picker Gallery at Kingston University, College of the Holy Cross (Worcester, Mass); and Queensland Art Gallery (Brisbane).

JAMES BUTLER

James Walter Butler, MBE RA FRBS RWA (1931-2022)

One of Britain's foremost figurative sculptors, James Butler was well known for both his public commissions, large and small, and his personal compositions. Having gained a thorough grounding in carving early in his career, he then developed equal mastery as a modeller. He created many cherished monuments in Britain and abroad that stand securely in a tradition that can be traced from Donatello through Charles Sargeant Jagger to Giacomo Manzù.

James Butler was born in New Cross, London, on 25 July 1931, the second of three children of Walter Butler, a stevedore, and his wife, Rosina (née Kingman). He enjoyed drawing from an early age, and received encouragement from his parents. In early childhood, he moved with his family to West Malling, in Kent, about six miles west of Maidstone, where his father had built a house.

During the Second World War, his father was conscripted to work on building projects. However, he sadly died of pneumonia when James was 10 years old, leaving his mother to support the family. She turned the house into a roadside café, called The Haven, and eventually remarried. During that time, she would try to persuade James to show his drawings to the customers, but he was reluctant to do so.

While at West Malling, James attended Maidstone Grammar School. He got on particularly well with one teacher, who was both his art master and the careers adviser. When he reached the age of 16, James told him that he wanted to go to art school, and was encouraged to do so.

James went to Maidstone School of Arts and Crafts, with the intention of becoming a painter. However, the foundation course introduced him to a wide range of artistic techniques and practices, and the opportunity to model clay proved a revelatory experience, soon sparking an obsession with sculpture.

While at Maidstone, James studied sculpture under Sydney Birnie Stewart, known as Jock. When Stewart moved to St Martin's School of Art, he encouraged James to join him there, and persuaded his mother to fund his further study. In moving back to London, he stayed with an aunt in Camberwell.

At St Martin's, James studied under Sydney Stewart and the Head of Sculpture, Walter Marsden, and had high regard for both of them. During James's last term at St Martin's, Marsden decided that his students had had no practical experience. As a result, he employed the stone carver, Gerald Giudici, to show them how to use a pointing machine to copy a plaster cast into stone. Though Giudici's demonstration did not go well, he became friendly with James and invited him to become an apprentice carver.

Once he had completed his National Diploma at St Martin's, James left Giudici temporarily in order to undertake two years of National Service. He served in the Army, working on codes with the Royal Signals, mostly in Germany. When on leave, he stayed with his mother, who had settled in West Norwood, South London.

On completing National Service, James worked again with Giudici as a full-time carver. During this period, he was involved in the carving of many architectural sculptures by William McMillan, Charles Wheeler and James Woodford, including the *Queen's Beasts* at Kew Gardens.

At the time that he returned to the employ of Giudici, he followed the advice of colleagues and enrolled in evening classes at the City and Guilds of London Art School. As a former Rome Scholar, his teacher, Bernard Sindall, directed him to the work of the Italian sculptors in the modelling tradition – Giacomo Manzù, Marino Marini and Medardo Rosso – and they would prove to be most influential in his development.

James was awarded the Beckwith Scholarship, and Sindall arranged for him to stay at the British School in Rome for about a month. While there, he was able to look closely at the work of Manzù and Marini, and also at the ancient art that had inspired them, especially that of the Etruscans.

When David McFall took over from Bernard Sindall at the City and Guilds, in 1956, Butler was offered a job teaching there. At first he refused, and took up a scholarship at the Royal College of Art. However, after being at the RCA for some time, he found that he lacked the freedom that he had had at the City and Guilds. So, in 1960, he returned and took up the teaching job. In order to focus on this new position, he also left the employ of Giudici.

Creating the atmosphere of an atelier, in which he and his students worked together in parity, James particularly enjoyed his early years of teaching. At the same time, he established himself as a sculptor, carving a reclining figure for a position outside the City and Guilds, in Cleaver Square, and beginning to exhibit at the Royal Academy. His success was marked, in 1964, by his election as an associate of the Royal Academy, making him the youngest academician at the time.

For a while, James lived alongside other artists, at the Abbey Art Centre, Barnet, and Digswell Arts Trust, Welwyn Garden City, Hertfordshire. Then, in 1966, he moved to Greenfield, Bedfordshire, and, for the next 20 years, lived and worked in the Victorian former village schoolhouse. During the late 1960s and early 1970s, James created stage sculptures for productions at the Royal Shakespeare Company at Stratford-upon-Avon, including *Julius Caesar* and *Coriolanus*, and at English National Opera in London. He also produced waxworks for Madame Tussauds, including one of The Beatles for its London premises and others of Rembrandt and his family for Amsterdam, in association with the designer, Timothy O'Brien.

Elected a full Royal Academician in 1972, James began to receive significant international commissions, including one of Jomo Kenyatta, the Kenyan President. The majestic 12 foot seated figure, placed in the centre of Nairobi, proved a turning point in his career. Most immediately, it led to a commission from Zambia for a monument to Freedom Fighters to stand outside Freedom House, in Lusaka.

In 1975, James gave up teaching at City and Guilds to concentrate full time on sculpture. In the same year, he began a lasting marriage to Angie Berry, who would become a journalist and author. They settled at Valley Farm, Radway, Warwickshire, and there brought up their four daughters, and James's daughter by a previous marriage.

James was elected a fellow of the Royal Society of British Sculptors in 1981. Demand for public commissions has continued both in the United Kingdom and abroad, with notable achievements including: *King Richard III* in the Castle Gardens, Leicester, commissioned by the Richard III Society (1977); the *Cippico Fountain*, Heriot-Watt University, Edinburgh, commissioned by the Constance Fund and awarded the Otto Beit Medal (1982); *Field Marshal Earl Alexander of Tunis*, at the Wellington Barracks, London, awarded the Silver Medal of the Royal Society of British Sculptors for the 'Best Work Exhibited to the Public' (1985); *Sir John Moore*, with attendant figures of Rifleman and Bugler, at the Sir John Moore Barracks, Winchester (1986); the *Memorial to the Green Howards*, a seated figure of a contemplative soldier, at Crépon, near the Normandy Landings (1996); and the *Memorial to the Fleet Air Arm*, the winged figure of Daedalus, which stands in the Embankment Gardens in London (2000).

In contrast to the towering figures for which he is so well known, James made designs for the Royal Mint: the Royal Seal of the Realm (2001); the 50 pence piece, commemorating Roger Bannister's 4 minute mile (2004); and the £5 coin to celebrate the 200th anniversary of the Battle of Trafalgar (2005).

Honours included election as a senior Royal Academician (2006) and the award of an MBE (2009). He was also a Visiting Professor at the Royal Academy Schools.

His recent monumental figurative sculptures include the *Rainbow Division Memorial*, a pietà placed, on 12 November 2011, at the site of the Battle of Croix Rouge Farm in Picardy, France. On 14 June 2015, his statue of *Her Majesty Queen Elizabeth II* in full garter robes was unveiled at Runnymede, Surrey, in celebration of the 800th anniversary of Magna Carta.

In 2020 he was awarded the Chevalier de l'Ordre des Arts et des Lettres (France).

James Butler died on 26 March 2022, aged 90, after a short illness.